MERMAIDS AND MASTODONS

MERMAIDS AND MASTODONS

A BOOK OF NATURAL & UNNATURAL HISTORY

Richard Carrington

With illustrations by
MAURICE WILSON
AND OTHERS

RINEHART & COMPANY, INC.
NEW YORK

FOR
MY MOTHER
who first introduced me
to animals and gave me the
chance to practise my trade

Contents

List of Plates

The American mastodon, a prehistoric elephant that may have been a contemporary of the first men of the American continent. *Reconstruction by Maurice Wilson*   *Frontispiece*

ix

LIST OF PLATES

List of Figures

LIST OF FIGURES

LIST OF FIGURES

xiii

Preface

THERE are many ways of looking at a subject, especially such a richly diversified subject as natural history. The professor of zoology in his classroom, and the bacteriologist in his laboratory; the duffle-coated bird-watcher ploughing through the mud of the Essex marshes, and the fossil collector chipping a dinosaur skeleton from its matrix under the burning New Mexican sun – each of these is following his own particular bent and making his own special contribution to unravelling the many tangled problems of the living world.

Compared to the skill and dedication of these workers the aims of this book are modest in the extreme. The reader will look in vain for original contributions to knowledge, and if he requires weighty pronouncements on the technicalities of research he will throw it aside disappointed. My object in writing it has been simply to collect together some of the more unusual and romantic facts concerning the several branches of natural science to which I am personally most attracted. I have followed no set scheme, but my own inclination, and these pages therefore contain a miscellany of facts, not only about animals living and extinct, but also about their discoverers, the old naturalists who wrote about them so fascinatingly, and even about the geology and geography of the lands in which they live.

On the other hand, many years spent in the company of professional naturalists and scientists has, I hope, caused me to submit to a necessary discipline. Even in an unpretentious popular work of this kind there is, I feel, a need for accurate and exact documentation. Thus, except in two or three cases where books and periodicals were not available in this country, I have made it a rule always to go back to the original sources to verify my facts. The only liberty I have taken in quotation is occasionally to modernize the spelling and punctuation where, as in some of the older books, they made the sense of the extract difficult to understand. All my sources, as well as a number of suggestions for further reading, are listed in the Bibliography on Page 233, and I hope they will be of use to readers who may wish to follow up any particular subject more closely.

The first part of the book is devoted mainly to fabulous animals, whose origin I have tried to trace in the real birds and beasts of the living world. In the second part I have made an excursion into the geological past to talk about some of the extinct creatures, no less extraordinary than the mermaid, the dragon and the rukh, which are now only known to us from their fossil bones. The third part brings us back to the present, and in particular to some animals and plants which, by all the laws, ought to be fossils, but are in fact very much alive. Finally, in the fourth part, I have described the passing of some of the animals which have only recently become extinct, and others whose existence is now very seriously threatened.

In thus wandering at will through the past and the present, trespassing into the realms of several sciences, I have made many friends, both in the writings of authors long since dead and among living authorities in different departments of natural history. To all these I owe a great debt. My obligations are no less to those who have put me on the track of new books or new ideas, and especially to the library staffs of the British Museum (Natural History) and the Zoological Society of London whose help has been at all times invaluable. Last, but not least, I feel that any writer on natural history owes his biggest debt of all to the animals who furnish the material for his work, and who give the Earth so much of its splendour. It is for once true to say, in the well-worn author's cliché, that without them this book could never have been written.

R.C.

PART ONE

Behind the Legends

CHAPTER ONE

The Natural History of Mermaids

Desinat in piscem mulier formosa superne
HORACE: *Ars Poetica*

Slow sailed the weary mariners and saw,
Betwixt the green brink and the running foam,
Sweet faces, rounded arms, and bosoms prest
To little harps of gold; and while they mused,
Whispering to each other half in fear,
Shrill music reach'd them on the middle sea.
TENNYSON: *The Sea Fairies*

FOR any one who could afford to pay 6½d for a four page broadsheet consisting mainly of advertisements, *The Times* of Friday, September 8th 1809 contained several exceptionally interesting and colourful paragraphs. For example, His Majesty the King of Wurttemberg had passed a law 'declaring every body out of his wits who presumed to talk freely or irreverently of his Royal person'. And a Marylebone lamplighter had been sent for trial for wantonly drawing his burner across the breeches of a respectable young Scotsman named Alexander Campbell.

But for connoisseurs of the picturesque a letter sandwiched inconspicuously between the Ship News and the Price of Stocks must surely have provided the highlight of the day's news. It was from a Mr William Munro, a schoolmaster of Thurso in Scotland, and was headed 'The Mermaid Seen on the Coast of Caithness'. The following is the substance of this singular communication:

DEAR SIR – About twelve years ago, when I was Parochial Schoolmaster at Reay, in the course of my walking on the shore of Sandside Bay, being a fine warm day in summer, I was induced to extend my walk towards Sandside Head, when my attention was arrested by the appearance of a figure resembling an unclothed human female, sitting upon a rock extending into the sea, and apparently in the action of combing its hair, which flowed around its shoulders, and

3

was of a light brown colour. The forehead was round, the face plump, the cheeks ruddy, the eyes blue, the mouth and lips of a natural form, resembling those of a man; the teeth I could not discover, as the mouth was shut; the breasts and abdomen, the arms and fingers of the size of a full grown body of the human species; the fingers, from the action in which the hands were employed, did not appear to be webbed, but as to this I am not positive. It remained on the rock three or four minutes after I observed it, and was exercised during that period in combing its hair, which was long and thick, and of which it appeared proud, and then dropped into the sea, from whence it did not reappear to me. I had a distinct view of its features, being at no great distance on an eminence above the rock on which it was sitting, and the sun brightly shining.

If the above narrative can in any degree be subservient towards establishing the existence of a phenomenon, hitherto almost incredible to naturalists, or to remove the scepticism of others, who are ready to dispute every thing which they cannot fully comprehend, you are welcome to it, from

Dear Sir

Your most obliged, and most humble servant,

(Signed) Wm. Munro

Mr Munro was not alone in his observation of this mysterious and romantic phenomenon. His letter to *The Times* had itself been prompted by the experience of a certain Miss Mackay and another girl, who had seen a creature of equally unusual physique bathing in a rough sea off the coast of Caithness earlier in the year. According to Miss Mackay, this creature had a face that was 'round and plump and of a bright pink hue'. Although not actually observed to have a comb, every now and then it would lift a slim white arm above the waves and toss back a mane of long green hair. Thus the two descriptions agreed together excellently and for a time there seemed every reason to hope that mermaids would be recognized as a valuable if unexpected addition to the marine fauna of Scotland.

Unfortunately, however, this romantic possibility was never to be realized. No further Scottish mermaids were seen, and in the absence of proof in the shape of a live specimen, or at least a corpse, naturalists preserved an aloof and dignified silence. Long before the end of the year the nine days' wonder was at an end, and Miss Mackay and Mr Munro relapsed once more into

4

the obscurity from which they had so briefly but gloriously emerged.

I have quoted this story at some length because it is a good example of the persistence into comparatively modern times of a legend that is nearly as old as the written records of man. There is not an age, and hardly a country in the world, whose folklore does not contain some reference to mermaids or to mermaid-like creatures. They have been alleged to appear in a hundred different places, ranging from the mist-covered shores of Norway and Newfoundland to the palm-studded islands of the tropic seas. Wherever they have been seen, the legends tell us that they have stirred up men's hearts to a strange mixture of emotions, – to wonder and fear, ecstasy and irresistible desire.

The persistence of the mermaid legend, and the similarity of so many of the reports from independent sources in different areas, suggests that it is based on more than an idle fantasy of the human imagination. It seems certain, as I shall try to show later, that some real animal or, more likely, a number of different animals lie behind the legend in its various forms. But even when this is realized we do not thereby gain a true insight into the subject. The natural history of mermaids cannot be understood, like that of mackerel or cod, by the methods of science alone. Even in reading Mr Munro's letter we feel there is something misleading, not to say unchivalrous, about his purely clinical description of mermaid anatomy, and his insistence on the sexless and impersonal pronoun 'it'. Mermaids, even if their legend proves to be partly rooted in scientific fact, are too glamorous a theme to be treated in this way. I therefore make no excuse for prefacing my discussion of mermaid natural history with a *resumé* of their romantic mythological past.

A long path of association and evolving tradition lies between the mermaid's most ancient recorded ancestor and the green-haired, ripe-breasted girl of later times, with her comb and mirror, who beguiled unsuspecting sailors to destruction with her beauty and her seductive songs. We cannot even be sure of the line of her descent, so quickly do legends evolve, intermingle and change. But we can at least say, if we are to accept the general opinion of the mythologists, that the most ancient ancestor of all the mermaids was, in all probability, not a woman but a man: and yet not quite a man according to our modern conception, but an animal turned god, who rose from the Erythraean sea to teach mortals the values of civilization, and who stood in their eyes for the mysterious processes of healing and fertility and the life-giving power of the sun.

The story is told in a fragment of ancient history preserved for us by Berosus the Chaldean, a priest and astronomer of Babylon, who lived in the third century B.C. 'The whole body of the animal', he says, 'was like that of a fish; and had under a fish's head another head, and also feet below, like those of a man joined to its fish's tail. He was endowed with reason, and his voice and language were articulate and human. And he gave men an insight into letters and sciences, and every kind of art – into everything, in short, which could tend to soften manners and humanize mankind.'

The name of this amiable creature was Oannes, the Babylonian fish god. He rose from the sea each morning, and at sunset plunged once more beneath the waves. Early pictures of Oannes represent him as having human form, but with a fish's head worn as a cap. The skin of the fish hangs from his shoulders like a cloak, the tail reaching below his thighs, and sometimes as low as his ankles. His appearance in this costume makes a good approximation to the description of him given by Berosus, but is still only remotely suggestive of the form of his mermaid descendants.

In the next stage of Oannes' development, however, as preserved in ancient sculptures at Khorsabad and elsewhere, his figure has become greatly simplified, and he is shown with the upper parts of a man and the lower parts and tail of a fish. In this form he is usually identified with the Babylonian water god Ea, and sometimes with the Biblical Dagon. But scholars are cautious about the association with Dagon, feeling that although Oannes and Ea were undoubtedly 'fishy', Dagon was more probably an Earth god particularly associated with corn. However this may be, it is now apparent that Oannes, with certain important differences, is approximating more nearly to the genus, if not the species, of the strange creature seen by Mr Munro off the coast of Scotland. The most obvious and fundamental difference, of course, is that of his sex.

Of the feminine deities to whom the mermaid owes her ancestry the earliest is the Semitic moon goddess, Atergatis, or

Derceto. She, like Oannes, was a fish deity, and was depicted at first with human extremities projecting from a fish-like cloak. But her form became altered also, so that in the words of Lucian, 'she had the half of a woman, and from the thighs

Atergatis (left), from a Phoenician coin, and Aphrodite drawn by Tritons, from a Corinthian coin

downwards a fish's tail'. Glamorous as she was, she had an eye to practical matters, for she issued an edict that no one should go fishing without a licence from herself. The dues from these licences doubtless made a welcome addition to the funds administered by her high priests.

The reasons for the fish-like shape of Oannes and his feminine counterpart, Atergatis, provide a good example of the way myths change and grow. I mentioned earlier how Oannes was associated with the life-giving power of the sun. The idea of a sun god is as old as Palaeolithic man, maybe even older, and he is usually the most powerful and influential deity in primitive cosmologies. Oannes himself was probably once exclusively a sun god, his quality as a civilizing power being a secondary attribute that grew up with the evolution of the world's first settled communities. But did not the sun rise at dawn from the sea, to fall into it once more at the close of the day? Then what more natural than that Oannes should be endowed with the shape of a man-fish, a supernatural power who came on land in the day time, spreading light and life, and plunged at night into the dark and mysterious wastes of the sea?

If these assumptions are correct, then Atergatis, the moon goddess, was endowed with her fish-like form because she was Oannes' feminine counterpart. Like him she rose from the surface of the ocean and returned to it at the end of her long journey across the night sky. She too, men argued, must be

7

amphibious, part human, part fish; but less physically powerful and still more mysterious than Oannes, like woman herself. Thus the first fish goddess came into being, and her qualities spread and grew like a rumour or a legend. She took on in her person, under her different guises, the many attributes that men have always ascribed to women – beauty, vanity, pride, cruelty, seductiveness and unattainable love. Atergatis, and her many counterparts in other mythologies, was not, we may feel, an unlikely or unworthy ancestor of the mermaid of later times.

As a result of the prestige of the great fish gods and goddesses who were so widely worshipped by men before the Christian era, several lesser supernatural beings grew up in similar form. Thus Aphrodite, who is sometimes identified with Atergatis and likewise rose from the sea, was served by two or more minor deities with human bodies and fishes' tails. These were the Tritons, who in addition to paying homage to Aphrodite, had certain powers of their own as sea gods, being able to calm the waves and rule the storm. The famous Sirens are also sometimes pictured in the form of mermaids, but this is not strictly accurate for they were first conceived as creatures with women's heads but bird-like, winged bodies. They nevertheless played an important part in the growth of the mermaid legend for they originated the idea of the fatal supernatural lover who lured mariners to their deaths, either by the beauty of their voices, which caused the sailors to leap from their ships, or by casting the ship itself to destruction on the rocky shore. This power was later transferred to the mermaids, and so the Sirens, like the Tritons, can be regarded as one of the links which joined the fish gods and fish goddesses of pre-Christian mythology with the more recent developments of mermaid lore.

The earliest naturalist to deal with mermaids in any detail was Pliny the Elder, whose famous *Natural History* appeared in the first century A.D. Pliny was a man of forthright character, a cavalry officer and a writer of military history, whom one could never have suspected of undue credulity. Yet he not only believed in mermaids, being convinced that they were real creatures, but cited the most illustrious personages to support his opinion. Philemon Holland, Pliny's seventeenth century

English translator, records his views on mermaids in such picturesque language and spelling that I cannot forbear quoting them in their original form. 'And as for the Meremaids', he says, 'it is no fabulous tale that goeth of them: for looke how painters draw them, so they are indeed: only their bodie is rough and skaled all over, even in those parts wherein they resemble a woman. For such a Meremaid was seene and beheld plainely upon a coast neere to the shore: and the inhabitants dwelling neer, heard it a farre off when it was a dying, to make pitteous mone, crying and chattering very heavily.'

No one in seventeenth century England would have regarded these words of Pliny's as particularly surprising. They might have questioned the finer points of the description, but the existence of mermaids was as firmly established as the existence of shrimps. They were regularly seen off the coast of Britain, and travellers brought back tales of encounters with them from every corner of the seven seas. Two examples from this period will suffice, both reported by seamen of great knowledge and experience whom it would be difficult to accuse of an exaggerated gift for fantasy.

I have taken the first from the stolid, prosaic narrative of the voyages of Henry Hudson, published in London in 1625. Here is recorded, in the most matter-of-fact language, an incident which occurred near Nova Zembla on one of Hudson's famous attempts to force the North West Passage:

This evening (June 15) one of our company, looking overboard, saw a mermaid, and, calling up some of the company to see her, one more of the crew came up, and by that time she was come close to the ship's side, looking earnestly on the men. A little after a sea came and overturned her. From the navel upward, her back and breasts were like a woman's, as they say that saw her; her body as big as one of us, her skin very white, and long hair hanging down behind, of colour black. In her going down they saw her tail, which was like the tail of a porpoise, speckled like a mackerel. Their names that saw her were Thomas Hilles and Robert Rayner.

The second mermaid report is taken from a description of the colony of Newfoundland by Sir Richard Whitbourne, a sea captain of Exmouth in Devon. Whitbourne had made numerous voyages to that country, and in 1620 he published his *Discourse and Discovery of New-found-land*, to give a picture of its amenities and to encourage new settlers. One of the more unusual episodes recorded reads as follows:

Now also I will not omit to relate something of a strange Creature, which I first saw there in the year 1610, in a morning early as I was standing by the River side, in the Harbour of St. Johns, which very swiftly came swimming towards me, looking cheerfully on my face, as it had been a woman: by the face, eyes, nose, mouth, chin, ears, neck and forehead, it seemed to be beautiful, and in those parts well proportioned, having round about the head many blue streaks resembling hair, but certainly it was no hair. . . . It swam towards the place where a little before I landed, and it did often look back towards me; whereby I beheld the shoulders and back down to the middle to be so square, white and smooth as the back of a man; and from the middle to the hinder part it was pointing in proportion something like a broad hooked Arrow: how it was in the forepart from the neck and shoulders I could not well discern. . . . It came shortly after to a Boat in the same Harbour (wherein one William Hawkridge, then my servant, was) and did put both his hands upon the side of the Boat, and did strive much to come in to him, and divers then in the same Boat; whereat they were afraid, and one of them struck it a full blow on the head, whereby it fell off from them. . . . This (I suppose) was a Mermaid or Merman.

Although we may dissent from this last opinion, it would be impossible to accuse such a sober and straightforward witness as Whitbourne of fraud or sensationalism. The episode obviously occurred as it was described, and it was the identity, not the existence, of the 'strange Creature' that a later and more sophisticated generation was to question. The mermaid, for the moment, continued to be firmly entrenched in popular belief.

The eighteenth century, which prided itself on its worldliness, cynicism, and good sense, was nevertheless as passionately addicted to mermaids as the preceding age. One of the main protagonists of their cause was François Valentijn, a Dutch colonial chaplain, who, in his *Natural History of Amboina*, published in 1726, gives numerous accounts of their appearances in the East Indies. The first section of his chapter on the fishes of Amboina is devoted to a detailed description of 'Zee-Menschen' and 'Zee-Wyven', a particularly glamorous example being depicted with other local fish on a composite plate. This was copied from a coloured drawing by one Samuel Fallours, official painter to the Dutch East India Company, which originally appeared in 1718 in a book called *'Poissons, Ecrevisses et Crabes ... des Isles Moluques.* The caption to this picture suggests that Fallours had encountered a different species of mermaid from any we have so far described, and reads as follows:

ZEE-WYF: A monster resembling a Siren caught on the coast of Borneo in the administrative district of Amboina. It was 59 inches long and in proportion as an eel. It lived on land for four days and seven hours in a barrel filled with water. From time to time it uttered little cries like those of a mouse. Although offered small fish, molluscs, crabs, crayfish, etc, it would not eat. After its death some excreta, like that of a cat, was found in its barrel.

The Amboina mermaid.
From Valentijn's *Natural History of Amboina* (1726)

The fame of this Amboina mermaid quickly spread into the most exalted circles. The original of her picture was presented to King George III of England, while His Imperial Majesty, Peter the Great, Czar of Russia, saw a copy of it in the office of Louis Renard, publisher at Amsterdam, and requested that further enquiries should be made of Valentijn. The latter unfortunately had little to add to what had already been said about this mermaid, but was prompted by the Czar's interest to record yet another mermaid encounter:

'I may say that I know for certain', he states, 'that in the year 1652 or 1653 a lieutenant in the service of the Company saw two of these beings in the gulf, near the village of Henne-telo, in the administrative district of Amboina. They were swimming side by side, which made him presume that one was male, the other female. Six weeks after, they reappeared in the same spot, and were seen by more than fifty persons. These monsters were of a greenish grey colour, having precisely the shape of human beings from the head to the waist, with arms and hands, but their bodies tapered away.'

Valentijn himself was quite convinced of the authenticity of this story, as of all the others he had related. 'If any narrative in the world deserves credit, it is this,' he asserts; 'for *not only one but two mermen* together were seen by so many eyewitnesses. Should the stubborn world, however, hesitate to believe it, it matters nothing; for there are people who would even deny the existence of such cities as Rome, Constantinpole or Cairo, simply because they themselves have not happened to see them.'

But this last sentence of Valentijn's does suggest that scepticism was increasing. As the early eighteenth century wore on, naturalists found it increasingly difficult to maintain even in their own minds a whole-hearted belief in the mermaid's real existence. The famous author of *The Natural History of Norway*, Erik Pontoppidan, dismisses a great deal of what is said about them as mere idle talk, mentioning particularly a merman who was reported to have spoken fluent Danish to two Senators, and a mermaid who, it was alleged, had foretold the birth of King Christian IV. 'When such fictions are mixed with the history of the Mermen,' he grumbles, 'and when that is re-presented as a prophet and an orator; when they give the Mermaid a melodious voice, and tell us that she is a fine singer; one need not wonder that so few people of sense will give credit to such absurdities; or that they even doubt the existence of such a creature.' Yet even Pontoppidan cannot bring himself to reject the mermaid altogether, for he follows his reservations with eight folio pages devoted to the 'true' natural history of the genus.

It would be possible to multiply the tales of mermaids seen, or reported seen, almost indefinitely. Many of these were obviously fictitious, and contained every element from the higher flights of alcoholic fancy down to plain bare-faced lying. For instance, there was the story of the exceptionally beautiful mermaid captured in the early eighteenth century by Manx fishermen and kept for several days in a house in the village before being returned to her native element. The only comment made by this creature as she rejoined her own people in the surf – a comment, moreover, that was distinctly heard by the fishermen standing on the shore to watch – was that human beings were so exceedingly ignorant that they threw away the water in which they had boiled eggs. Other stories, like those recorded by Hudson, Whitbourne, Valentijn and Pontoppidan, seem undoubtedly to have had a substratum of fact, while others again are borderline cases. One of these last is the legend of the man-fish who is said to have conducted Indian tribes from Asia to North America, and whose anatomy seems to belong partly to zoology and partly to myth. Another is the story of the merman seen by several persons on the coast of Martinique who was approached so closely that it was seen to wipe its hands across its face and actually heard to blow its nose.

I have unfortunately no space here to elaborate these promising themes. There is, however, one further aspect of mermaid lore that must be touched upon before we proceed to the less frivolous zoological aspects of the subject. Despite the growing momentum of scientific knowledge, a widespread belief in mermaids, which contained wonder but no scepticism, persisted among certain classes of the community until well into the reign of Queen Victoria. We have already seen the serious approach to the subject made by Mr Munro and sanctioned by the august authority of *The Times*. By the middle of the century little change had occurred in this attitude except among the cognoscenti, and enterprising showmen had decided that the time was now ripe to take advantage of it. Hence the sudden appearance in certain rather dubious quarters of nineteenth century London of 'stuffed mermaids', which it was alleged had been caught along a variety of mysterious and romantic shores somewhere east of Suez and brought to London especially for the delectation of the public.

Francis Buckland in his *Curiosities of Natural History*, published between 1858 and 1866, records several instances of the display of these oddities. The most famous was that shown in London at the Egyptian Hall in the 1830's which was sold to two Italian brothers for 40,000 dollars and ended up as the subject of an embittered legal wrangle. Buckland himself gives a description of another stuffed mermaid that was established in 1858 in the back parlour of the White Hart at Spitalfields. It was between three and four feet long and was obligingly removed by the publican from its glass case so that Buckland could examine it. According to his description it was of the regulation mermaid pattern, half fish and half 'human', with hideous parchment-like ears standing well forward, a snub nose, the forehead wrinkled into a frown, and the lips curled into a ghastly grin. To establish its quasi-human nature beyond a doubt the lower jaw was equipped with an unmistakable human incisor tooth. A close examination of this repellent but fascinating object revealed that the upper part of its body consisted of the head, trunk and arms of a monkey, while the lower half, to which it was most carefully stitched, consisted of the skin of a fish which Buckland unromantically conjectured to be hake.

This particular composite mermaid had been made by an enterprising bird-stuffer in the West End, but the main centre of the art was probably Japan. According to Andrew Steinmetz's fascinating book *Japan and Her People*, published in 1859, Japanese fishermen found the traffic in artificial mermaids an invaluable means of supplementing their income. The system was briefly this. First the mermaid itself was artfully manufactured out of a monkey and a fish. The fisherman would then give out that the creature had been taken alive in his nets, but had shortly afterwards died. Profit accrued from two sources. First there was the money paid by the curious to inspect the body. The fisherman would then announce that shortly before the mermaid expired she had predicted a fatal epidemic from which the only protection would be the wearing of her own picture as a charm. Naturally the fisherman had a plentiful supply of such pictures ready to hand, and there can have been few of his superstitious countrymen who dared to tempt providence by going away without one.

Europe saw many of these Japanese mermaids during the nineteenth century, mostly as catchpennies in public exhibitions. The great American showman, P. T. Barnum, was particularly adept at exploiting them in his sideshows and fun fairs – a process he used to describe with obvious relish in a lecture

Lee's Japanese mermaid. From *Sea Fables Explained*

aptly entitled 'Humbug'. Other Japanese mermaids were to be found in the private collections of naturalists and curio hunters. The sphinx-like and somewhat gruesome specimen which I have illustrated here belonged to Henry Lee, naturalist of the Brighton Aquarium. Even today there is, I am told, a distinguished Cambridge professor who possesses an admirably preserved specimen, and has spent many agreeable hours in X-raying its interior.

I think I have now said enough to show the extraordinary vitality of the mermaid legend, which has caused it to persist for nearly 3,000 years and to be carried to every country in the world. It only remains to enquire why this should have been. In the first place there was the association of mermaids with the all-powerful sun god of early pagan religion, which undoubtedly gave the legend its original impetus. Secondly, there was the additional significance it acquired in course of time by association with the concept of ideal, but fatal, love embodied in the person of a remote and mysterious feminine being who could never be finally possessed by a living man. This concept appealed to the basic sexual and we may perhaps dare to add, even in a psychological age, spiritual instincts of mankind. The mermaid was the princess of medieval chivalry, the nineteenth century romantic's *idée fixe*, and the modern *femme fatale* rolled into one. But even when these emotional factors are taken into account they cannot explain many of the more prosaic and factual mermaid reports that have appeared from time to time. In some at least of these, it seems certain that a real animal was involved, which became 'transformed' into a mermaid by the expectant attention of the superstitious mariners who witnessed it.

It is perhaps unfortunate that the animal that has been cast most often in the role of mermaid goes by the unromantic popular name of sea-cow. For once, however, science has been kinder and more romantic and termed the order to which these real-life mermaids belong the Sirenia, or sirens. Until just over a hundred years ago this order of the animal kingdom was represented by three different genera, but the largest and most extraordinary of them, *Rhytina stelleri*, or Steller's sea-cow, is now extinct and will be dealt with later. It is not in any case likely that *Rhytina* could ever have been mistaken for a mermaid, except a very robust one, for it grew regularly to a length of twenty-five feet or more. The honour is therefore left to its smaller surviving relatives, the manatee and the dugong.

Both these creatures come from the tropics, the manatee frequenting the estuaries and big rivers of the African and American Atlantic coasts, the dugong being found in the Indian Ocean and along the shores of Australia and the East Indies. Their charm, at least as regards their appearance, is limited, but the details of their anatomy do bear some relation to that traditionally ascribed to mermaids. For instance their bodies are only slightly larger than a human being's, and unlike most mammals they have their breasts, or mammae, situated well forward on the trunk near the flipper-like forelimbs. There are no rear limbs at all and the body tapers to a rounded, and horizontally flattened tail. But despite these peculiarities, they are a very poor substitute for the seductive sea maidens of mythology. The thick and protruding upper lip is cleft in the middle for greater ease in cropping vegetation, and while the face of the manatee is almost hairless, the dugong is decidedly whiskered. The expression of both creatures, if harmless, is a trifle vacant, and one is additionally disconcerted to learn that their nearest animal relations are probably the elephant and the tapir. As Henry Lee remarks, distance must lend enchantment to the view, for it would be a very impressionable and imaginative sailor who, even after many weeks at sea without the company

A manatee. From Lee's *Sea Fables Explained*

of women, could be allured by the charms of a bristly-muzzled dugong, or mistake the snorting of a wallowing manatee for the love song of a mermaid.

But in addition to the shape of the manatees and dugongs, there are other factors that confirm their association with the mermaid legend. The dugong especially is said to suckle its young with the upper part of its body projecting from the water, holding the baby dugong to its breast with one flipper. If disturbed, the animal will plunge beneath the surface, often flicking its tail in the air as it does so. The young have also been heard to utter the doleful whimpering cries associated with some of the reports.

Many of the mermaid stories from the coasts of Africa and Asia have almost certainly been inspired by a distant or indistinct view of a dugong or manatee in the act of submerging; but it is obvious that such an explanation will not hold good for the vision vouchsafed to Mr Munro off the coast of Caithness, for the range of the Sirenia is entirely confined to the tropic coasts. The animal most likely to account for the various appearances of mermaids in cold and temperate latitudes is therefore probably one of the world's thirty species of seals.

There are three different families of seals comprised in the Pinnepedia, or 'fin feet', as this sub-order is scientifically termed. The Otariidae, or eared seals, and the Odobaenidae, or walruses, may on occasion have been responsible for mermaid reports – in fact the man-fish of the North American Indians was in my opinion almost certainly a walrus; but Mr Munro's mermaid and others reported from British waters were probably members of the third family, the Phocidae, or true seals. Two British members of this group are well known. The common seal, *Phoca vitulina*, is common in Shetland and Orkney, and down the east coast of Britain as far as the Wash. It is also found on the west coast, but here it is largely replaced by the second British species, the Atlantic seal, *Halichoerus grypus*.

Not everyone will agree that seals could in any circumstances be mistaken for mermaids, and certainly when they are seen at close quarters in a zoo or under similar controlled conditions, the theory is a little difficult to swallow. But in a storm tossed sea off the Scottish coast, or seen at a distance from a cliff top, the likeness is not really so very far fetched. The body of the

1a A dugong suckling its young. From Emerson Tennent's
Natural History of Ceylon (1861)

1b The common seal, *Phoca vitulina,* in a mermaid-like pose.

phocid seals tapers to a point in the same way as that of the Sirenia, and their hind limbs are permanently extended backwards, so that the rear part of the trunk strongly resembles the typical mermaid tail. Moreover, the plump, rounded, expressive face of the seal, its soft, intelligent eyes, and handlike fore-flippers give it a most human character, which is still further emphasized when, as often occurs, it poises itself in the water with only the upper part of its body protruding.

To prove this likeness, Henry Lee cites an occasion when he was sailing off the mouth of the river Maas near the Hook of Holland and a seal appeared in the attitude described above. It watched the yacht go by with the greatest curiosity, then dived and took up its station once more in the waters ahead. It repeated the process three times and could so easily have been mistaken for a human form that one of the occupants of the yacht thought it was a boy who had swum off from the shore on a begging expedition. Anyone who has watched the behaviour of seals when their interest and curiosity, but not their fear, has been aroused, will know that this is by no means an unlikely incident.

The natural history of mermaids, therefore, seems in many of its aspects to be safely comprised within the natural history of sea-cows and seals. No longer, with Philip Gosse, can we entertain the wistful hope 'that green-haired maidens with oary tails lurk in the ocean caves, and keep mirrors and combs upon their rocky shelves'. But as I said at the beginning of this chapter, the natural history of mermaids cannot be understood by the methods of natural science alone. These hauntingly beautiful goddesses of the sea, full of mystery and danger, were surely conjured from the chaos of the waters in answer to some primal human need. Their genus and species may not be carefully docketed in the *Nomenclator Zoologicus*, but their reality in terms of poetic truth is firmly established in the impassioned imagination of men.

CHAPTER TWO

The Great Sea Serpent

... and though they be hid from my sight in the bottom of the
sea, thence will I command the serpent, and he shall bite them.

AMOS: *Ch.*9 *v.*3

Strange things come up to look at us –
The masters of the deep.

19th CENTURY NAVAL SONG:
The Return of the Admiral

I MAKE no apology for devoting a chapter of this book to that
most romantic and controversial of all mystery animals, the
great sea serpent. Much has already been written about it, and
its reputation has fallen lately into disrepute: scientists wince
at the very mention of its name, while even newspaper editors
who a few years ago were clamouring for its services in the
tedious intervals between rapes and political crises, have become more moderate in their enthusiasm. But the subject of sea
serpents, like all genuine mysteries, is inexhaustible. It will be
talked about and argued over for as long as man has one ounce
of wonder and curiosity left in his nature. And in spite of the
scepticism of the experts, a real sea serpent is even now, I feel,
as likely to emerge from the sea and confound our human
theories as was the coelacanth *Latimeria* a couple of years before
the war.

Much of the loss of face suffered by the sea serpent has been
due to the misguided enthusiasm of its protagonists. Too many
rash statements and extravagant claims have been made on its
behalf, and one can hardly blame the professional naturalists
for becoming a trifle weary of being told that they must accept
as sea serpents creatures and objects that are obviously seals,
whales or floating tree trunks. On the other hand many reports
are obviously well-reasoned, competent and sincere, and cannot
be so easily dismissed.

A plea for the impartial judgement of sea serpent stories
was made as long ago as 1755 by that great natural historian,

20

Erik Pontoppidan, Bishop of Bergen. I quote from the second volume of his *Natural History of Norway*, which contains a chapter entirely devoted to 'certain Sea-monsters, or strange and uncommon Sea-animals'.

'Were it possible', he writes, 'that the sea could be drained of its waters, and emptied by some extraordinary accident, what incredible numbers, what infinite variety of uncommon and amazing Sea-monsters would exhibit themselves to our view, which are now entirely unknown! Such a sight would at once determine the truth of many hypotheses concerning Sea-animals, whose existence is disputed, and looked upon as chimerical. I will allow they may be uncertain, because we have but few opportunities to determine this point by such sure evidence as would leave no room for doubt; but at the same time this is certain, that as on the one side we ought not to be too credulous, and believe the idle tales and improbable stories that every fisherman or sailor relates, either on the credit of one of his companions, or from what he has seen himself, when embellished with a great many additions and variations, concerning strange and frightful sea-monsters: yet I am of opinion that the other extreme deviates as far from the truth; namely, when we will not believe things strange and uncommon tho', according to the unchangeable law of nature, possible, because we cannot have so evident and clear a demonstration of it as we might; by this way of arguing, all historic faith would be destroyed. One might as well doubt whether there are Hottentots; for tho' the number of witnesses be much greater in that case, still that does not alter the nature of the knowledge; it only raises it to a higher degree of certainty.'

This, I feel, is a pretty fair statement of what our approach to the sea serpent problem should be. But I do not propose in this chapter to dogmatize about whether or not the sea serpent actually exists. Too much hot air has already been expended on this fruitless question, which can only be finally settled when someone takes a cinematograph film at close quarters, or delivers a sea serpent, dead or alive, to the Zoo. Instead I intend to describe a few of the more dramatic alleged appearances of the sea serpent, and to examine some of the theories proposed to explain them. In this way it may be possible to judge how often there has been a known but unrecognized animal 'behind the legend', and how often we must continue to accept the fascinating possibility that a giant unknown creature still lurks in the abysses of the sea.

The earliest historical mention of the sea serpent occurs in Aristotle's *Historia Animalium*, written in the fourth century B.C. 'In Libya', he says, 'the serpents are very large. Mariners sailing along that coast have told how they have seen the bones of many oxen which, it was apparent to them, had been devoured by the serpents. And as their ships sailed on, the serpents came to attack them, some of them throwing themselves on a trireme and capsizing it.'

Other classical authorities have equally hair-raising tales to tell. In Pliny's *Natural History*, for instance, we can read how a Greek squadron, sent on a voyage of discovery by Alexander the Great, was thrown into confusion by sea serpents thirty feet long in the Persian Gulf. And the Latin author Valerius Maximus, writing in the first century A.D., quotes Livy concerning a gigantic aquatic monster which terrorized even the stolid Roman legionaries during the Punic Wars, and had to be liquidated by balistas and other primitive but powerful forms of artillery usually reserved for the seige of fortified towns.

We must regretfully admit that these stories are more picturesque than plausible. They were probably based on travellers' tales of pythons, and reports from fishermen of conger eels, or genuine water snakes. It is easy to understand how such accounts became distorted and exaggerated with constant repetition, especially when one reflects how common and tempting is the desire to impress. The practice can in fact still be studied at first hand in any good angling inn.

The descendants of these fearsome monsters survived in the writings of natural historians, if not in the sea, until well into the Middle Ages, when their main habitat seems to have been the coasts of northern Europe. The sixteenth century Archbishop of Upsala, Olaus Magnus, whose famous *History of the Northern People* first appeared in 1555, gives us the following graphic picture of a gigantic sea serpent, measuring 200 feet long and 20 feet thick, which was frequently reported by sailors off the Norwegian mainland. 'He hath commonly hair hanging from his neck a Cubit long, and sharp Scales, and is black, and he hath flaming shining eyes. This snake disquiets the Shippers, and he puts up his head on high like a pillar, and catcheth away men, and he devours them.' Such a sight must indeed have disquieted the shippers, and we are not surprised to learn that it also presaged 'some wonderful change of the Kingdom near at hand; namely that the Princes shall die, or be banished; or some Tumultuous Wars shall presently follow'. Such fantastic and magical creatures were widely believed in until as recently as the eighteenth century, and are imaginatively figured in many of the old natural histories by Gesner, Topsell, Aldrovandi, and others.

A typical sixteenth century sea serpent. From Gesner's *Historiae Animalium* (1551-87)

But in the 1730s a new element begins to creep into the sea serpent story. Instead of highly coloured variations on a traditional theme, purveyed at second, third or hundredth hand by simple seamen, we have now for the first time an eyewitness report by a responsible person whose integrity was so far beyond reproach that he was to end his days as an Archbishop. This witness was the Norwegian missionary Hans Egede, who while on a voyage to Greenland in 1734 reported the following extraordinary incident, which took place near the Danish Colony of Good Hope on the Davis Straits, Greenland:

Anno 1734, July. On the 6th appeared a very terrible sea-animal, which raised itself so high above the water, that its head reached above our maintop. It had a long, sharp snout, and blew like a whale, had broad, large flappers, and the body was, as it were, covered with a hard skin, and it was very wrinkled and uneven on its skin; moreover on the lower part it was formed like a snake, and when it went under water again, it cast itself backwards, and in doing so it raised its tail above the water, a whole ship-length from its body. That evening we had very bad weather.

The sea serpent seen by Hans Egede, July 6th 1734. From Pontoppidan's *Natural History of Norway*

This factual account, unembellished with sensational trimmings, has the stamp of a genuine observation. It was followed twelve years later by another appearance of the monster in northern waters, this time between Trondhjem and Molde on the Norwegian coast. The witnesses, of whom the chief was one Lorenz von Ferry, Royal Commander and Pilot General at Bergen, committed their testimony to paper and swore to its truth before a Norwegian court. Their ship at the time of the encounter was close inshore at a place called Jule-Naess, on a calm, hot day in the August of 1746. The first that von Ferry knew of any unusual circumstance impending was a murmuring from the crew, some of whom had sighted the sea serpent in the ship's path. It was heading towards them, and as it passed by, von Ferry ordered that the boat should be turned about and go in pursuit. But unfortunately, the oarsmen were unable to keep up with the creature (perhaps through lack of enthusiasm for the chase), and when in consequence von Ferry gave it a burst of small shot it immediately sank from sight and did not reappear.

This monster of von Ferry's was of a different pattern from that seen by Egede, and I append his own description of it for comparison. As quoted by Pontoppidan, von Ferry writes:

The head of this sea-serpent, which it held more than two feet above the surface of the water, resembled that of a horse. It was of a greyish colour, and the mouth was quite black and very large. It had large black eyes and a long white mane, which hung down to the surface of the water. Besides the head and neck, we saw seven or eight folds, or coils, of this snake, which were very thick, and as far as we could guess there was a fathom's distance between each fold.

In later reports of sea serpents creatures are described which often have a family likeness to one or other of these animals seen by Egede and von Ferry. Many of the descriptions mention either a long snake-like form exhibiting characteristic coils or humps, or alternatively a creature having a serpentine head and neck, but with a more massive humped body, and flappers. Von Ferry's 'mane' is also a common feature of several reports, although descriptions of its shape and colour vary from witness to witness. In general we cannot help being more struck by the likeness of the several accounts than by their differences.

With the dawn of the nineteenth century, sea serpent reports began to occur in better documented form. The earliest episode concerns a creature which became widely known in the Press as 'the animal of Stronsa', and is worth relating if only for its entertaining sequel, in which English and Scottish anatomists found themselves unexpectedly locked in mortal combat. The carcase of this famous monster had become stranded on some sunken rocks off the island of Stronsa (now spelt Stronsay) in the Orkneys in 1808, where it was sighted on September 26th by a party of fishermen. Several witnesses went to inspect the carcase, which was at once heralded as being that of a genuine sea serpent. Excitement ran high, and a sworn deposition together with measurements, a drawing, and several fragments of the corpse, including part of the skull, were sent to the Royal Museum of Edinburgh University. Here the Scottish naturalists rose nobly to the occasion. Dr John Barclay, a prominent member of the Wernerian Natural History Society of Edinburgh read a paper to that distinguished body confirming that the animal of Stronsa was a creature previously unknown to science. His colleagues seem to have agreed with him, for no record can be found of a single dissentient voice. But unfortunately for these learned gentlemen, their verdict seems to have contained more patriotism than science. A few months later Sir Everard Home, the celebrated surgeon and anatomist of the

The animal of Stronsa. From the *Memoirs of the Wernerian Natural History Society* (1811)

Royal College of Surgeons in London, became interested in the affair and applied to Stronsa for further remains. He was forwarded in reply two vertebrae that had luckily been preserved by one of the J.P.s who had taken the witnesses' depositions. From these, to the consternation of the Edinburgh naturalists, he declared that far from being an unknown monster the animal of Stronsa was simply a large specimen of *Squalus maximus*, the basking shark. The effect of this bombshell on its partisans beyond Hadrian's wall can well be imagined. For nearly fifty years, in scientific papers and the Press, Scottish professors fought a stubborn rearguard action to defend the unique character of their sea serpent. But their cause was doomed from the start, and when in 1849 even a Scottish authority, Professor Goodsir of Edinburgh, came out firmly on the side of *Squalus maximus*, there was really nothing further to be said. The matter was finally summed up in a letter by Dr James Ritchie, Keeper of the Natural History Department of the Royal Scottish Museum, to Commander Rupert T. Gould, author of that fascinating, if prejudiced book, *The Case for the Sea Serpent*: 'As regards the identity of the animal of Stronsa', he writes, 'I should say that no competent zoologist, who examined the figures in the Wernerian Society's Volume I of 1811, would have had any hesitation in saying that the representations . . . belonged to a cartilaginous fish. The remarks by Dr Barclay on the remains . . . show a zoological incompetence so great that I am surprised that the Society published them.'

So much, then, for the animal of Stronsa, but the next appearance of the sea serpent could by no means be so easily explained. This occured in August 1817 in the waters of Gloucester Harbour, Massachusetts, U.S.A., and was the subject of a comprehensive report published by the Linnaean Society of New England. I will begin with a quotation from the introductory note to this remarkable document which sets the scene in clear and precise terms:

In the month of August 1817, it was currently reported on various authorities, that an animal of very singular appearance had been recently and repeatedly seen in the harbour of Gloucester, Cape Ann, about thirty miles distant from Boston. It was said to resemble a serpent in its general form and motions, to be of immense size, and to move with wonderful rapidity; to appear on the surface of the water only in calm and bright weather; and to seem jointed or like a number of buoys or casks following each other in a line.

In consequence of these reports, at a meeting of the Linnaean Society of New England, holden at Boston on the 18th day of August, the Hon. JOHN DAVIS, JACOB BIGELOW, M.D. and FRANCIS C. GRAY Esq. were appointed a Committee to collect evidence with regard to the existence and appearance of any such animal.

Few committees can have been charged with a more unusual or fascinating task, and the triumvirate set to work with enthusiasm and efficiency. The day following their appointment they wrote to Mr Lonson Nash, a Justice of the Peace at Gloucester, asking him to collect sworn depositions from the witnesses of the 'strange sea animal'. Their letter stressed that the examination should be made as quickly as possible, that the persons examined should be asked not to communicate their statements to each other until they were committed to paper, and that only those who professed actually to have seen the monster were to give evidence at all. Included in the letter were twenty-five admirably framed questions, designed to elicit from the witnesses the maximum of information with the minimum of verbiage, and at the same time to present a clear idea of exactly what each witness had seen.

This procedure resulted in eight depositions from Gloucester, which were despatched by Nash to the Committee with commendable promptness on August 28th. Although the names of the witnesses are not strictly relevant to the story, they possess in themselves such a period charm that I cannot forbear quoting them: – Amos Story, mariner; Solomon Allen, Ship master; Epes Ellery, Ship master; William H. Foster, merchant; Matthew Gaffney, Ship carpenter; James Mansfield, merchant; John Johnston, jun., 'of the age of seventeen years'; and William B. Pearson, merchant. The Committee also took three depositions in Boston and one from a Captain Elkanah Finney of Plymouth who had reported a similar occurence two years previously.

Briefly, the tale revealed by this quite formidable company of witnesses was as follows:—

About midday on August 10th 1817 Amos Story was sitting on the shore of Gloucester Harbour when he saw about 150 yards away a strange animal with a turtle-like head projecting ten to twelve inches above the water. It was in view for an hour and a half, and at times exposed up to twelve feet of its total length. Story estimated that the animal was of about the thickness of a man and could move at the surprisingly fast speed of 30 miles an hour. It remained in Gloucester Harbour until August 23rd before finally disappearing. In the meantime the other witnesses added many details to this somewhat flimsy sketch. Solomon Allen estimated the creature's length at between 80 and 90 feet, confirming the reptilian appearance of the head, and adding that the body appeared to be jointed from head to tail so that a series of humps or bunches rose about 8 or 10 inches above the water. Epes Ellery and Matthew Gaffney observed that the serpent, if such it was, took no notice of boats or men, but seemed often to be indulging in play by making slow sinuous turns in the water. Even when Gaffney took a pot shot at it with his gun its only reaction was to submerge for a short period and reappear 100 yards away to continue playing as before. Opinions differed as to whether its skin was smooth or scaly, but there was general agreement that the body was limbless and snake-like and exhibited the vertical sinuosities or humps first described by Allen.

After collecting so much valuable evidence which, taken together, gave a remarkably clear picture of the sea serpent's size, shape and behaviour, the investigating Committee had every reason to pat itself on the back. Unfortunately, however, as we have already seen with the animal of Stronsa, sea serpents are not averse to having a little quiet amusement at the expense of their scientific investigators. The present case was no exception. A month or so after the sea serpent had left Gloucester Harbour a boy found a small black snake near the beach of Loblolly cove on the eastern shore of Cape Ann. The snake was killed with a pitchfork by the boy's father and taken by a neighbour who had purchased it to the investigating Committee. The suggestion was that the sea serpent had laid eggs on the shore and that this was one of its offspring.

The Committee was delighted by this idea and promptly had the snake dissected. To their excitement they found that it had the same bunches on its back that so many witnesses had described as characterizing the sea serpent. This caused them to dub it forthwith *Scoliophis atlanticus*, or 'the flexible snake of the Atlantic', and they devoted four pages of their Report to its possible relationship with the creature seen in Gloucester Harbour. Their verdict was that the two animals almost certainly belonged to the same species, and it was therefore extraordinarily unfortunate when the great French zoologist Henri Ducrotay de Blainville pointed out the following year that the baby sea serpent was in fact a somewhat diseased specimen of *Coluber constrictor*, the common black snake. This revelation apparently reduced the Committee to a stunned and shamefaced silence, and was especially regrettable in that it discredited the real value of much of the rest of their Report. Rightly or wrongly, the Gloucester sea serpent and its strange progeny were henceforward consigned by most people to the limbo of classic fishing stories.

After the sensational events of 1817 the sea serpent seems to have gone into temporary retirement. A few desultory reports came in, but none was particularly convincing or supported by the testimony of sufficiently numerous or well qualified witnesses. This comparative lull was, however, enlivened by a number of elaborate sea serpent hoaxes, not to mention at least two downright frauds. The first of these was perpetrated by a certain Captain Richard Rich, who actually put to sea at the end of 1817 to capture the sea serpent and bring it back to Boston as a trophy. *Scoliophis atlanticus* itself apparently eluded him, but he did succeed in capturing a tunny which he exhibited as the sea serpent in a dime show. This stratagem of course deceived no one, and Rich, to avoid the penalties of his dishonesty, was compelled to admit instead to stupidity by saying that he had made a genuine mistake.

The second sea serpent fraud was conducted on an altogether more exalted plane. It was inspired by one of those entertaining charlatans who are often found on the fringes of science, and manage to combine the shadiest activities with a disarming enthusiasm and even sometimes with real knowledge. His name was Dr Albert C. Koch, and in spite of his love of the sensational

Hydrarchos sillimani, as exhibited in 1845 by Dr Albert Koch. From Oudemans' *The Great Sea Serpent*

he seems to have been an industrious and talented collector of fossil bones. He reached the peak of his notoriety in 1845 when it was announced in New York that he was about to show a genuine sea serpent skeleton on Broadway. He had christened the creature *Hydrarchos sillimani*, in alleged honour of the famous American professor, Benjamin Silliman, but the cynical were not slow to point out that the name might have a twofold significance. This, in fact, proved to be the case. The bones of the skeleton were identified as belonging to several specimens of an extinct whale known as *Zeuglodon* which their enterprising owner had excavated in different parts of Alabama and strung together in the form of a 'sea serpent', 114 feet long.

Koch does not seem to have been in the least daunted by this exposure, and doubtless made a considerable sum of money before the bones finally found their way to Germany to be correctly reassembled.

I come now to the most famous of all sea serpent yarns. It relates to the dramatic and spectacular episode of August 6th 1848 witnessed by the Captain and six members of the crew of H.M.S. *Daedalus*. The *Daedalus* was a corvette returning from service in the East Indies, and in those days, of course, before

The sea serpent when first seen from H.M.S. *Daedalus*, August 6th 1848.
From *The Illustrated London News*, October 28th 1848

the building of the Suez Canal, she had to pass by the Cape of Good Hope. When she arrived at Plymouth at 6.40 a.m. on October 4th, her crew were full of stories of a giant sea serpent that had been seen by some of their number in the South Atlantic about 300 miles off the African coast. A paragraph giving a garbled version of the affair quickly found its way into the evening papers, and eventually, on October 10th, into *The Times*.

That morning, we may suppose, some senior member of the First Sea Lord's staff was seated quietly at breakfast when this paragraph caught his eye. It is not difficult to imagine the result. The same day a brief and pointed minute went from the Admiralty to Admiral Sir W. H. Gage, Devonport, asking him to find out from Captain M'Quhae of the *Daedalus* what the devil he was talking about. Captain M'Quhae's reply is so interesting, and in addition so convincingly expressed, that I feel it best to let it speak for itself:

Her Majesty's Ship *Daedalus*,
Hamoaze, Oct. 11.

SIR – In reply to your letter of this day's date, requiring information as to the truth of a statement published in *The Times* newspaper, of a sea-serpent of extraordinary dimensions having been seen from Her Majesty's ship *Daedalus* under my command, on her passage from the East Indies, I have the honour to acquaint you, for the information of my Lords Commissioners of the Admiralty, that at 5 o'clock p.m. on the 6th of August last, in latitude 24° 44′ S., and longitude 9° 22′ E., the weather dark and cloudy, wind fresh from the N.W., with a long ocean swell from the S.W., the ship on the port tack heading N.E. by N., something very unusual was seen by Mr Sartoris, midshipman, rapidly approaching the ship from before the beam. The circumstance was immediately reported by him to the officer of the watch, Lieut. Edgar Drummond, with whom and Mr William Barrett, the Master, I was at the time walking the quarter-deck. The ship's company were at supper.

On our attention being called to the object it was discovered to be an enormous serpent, with head and shoulders kept about four feet constantly above the surface of the sea, and as nearly as we could approximate by comparing it with the length of what our main-topsail yard would show in the water, there was at the very least 60 feet of the animal *à fleur d'eau*, no portion of which was, to our perception, used in propelling it through the water, either by vertical or horizontal undulation. It passed rapidly, but so close under our lee quarter, that had it been a man of my acquaintance I should easily have recognized his features with the naked eye; and it did not, either in approaching the ship or after it had passed our wake, deviate in the slightest degree from its course to the S.W., which it held on at the pace of from 12 to 15 miles per hour, apparently on some determined purpose.

The diameter of the serpent was about 15 or 16 inches behind the head, which was, without any doubt, that of a snake, and it was never, during the 20 minutes that it continued in sight of our glasses, once below the surface of the water; its colour a dark brown, with yellowish white about the throat. It had no fins, but something like a mane of a horse, or rather a bunch of seaweed, washed about its back. It was seen by the quartermaster, the boatswain's mate, and the man at the wheel, in addition to myself and officers above mentioned.

I am having a drawing of the serpent made from a sketch taken immediately after it was seen, which I hope to have ready for transmission to my Lords Commissioners of the Admiralty by tomorrow's post.

I have, etc,

PETER M'QUHAE, Captain.

To Admiral Sir W. H. Gage, G.C.H., Devonport.

The drawing mentioned in the report is no longer extant, but its loss is made good by a set of pictures which appeared in the *Illustrated London News* on October 28th 1848. These had been prepared by the magazine's own artists supervised by M'Quhae himself, so their authenticity is beyond question.

The pictures and the report taken together certainly suggest that some genuinely unknown animal had been observed, but the naturalists of the time were not disposed to accept this view and a number of ingenious proposals were put forward to explain the whole episode away. The first to go into action was Professor Sir Richard Owen, the Hunterian Professor of Comparative Anatomy and Physiology at the Royal College of Surgeons, who had an international reputation as an anatomist and zoologist, and was shortly to be the spearhead of an attack on Charles Darwin's 'new-fangled' conception of human evolution. His case against the *Daedalus* sea serpent is too long to be discussed in detail, but it was well argued and, to many of his colleagues, convincing. He firmly believed from M'Quhae's description that the creature concerned must have been not a serpent but a warm-blooded mammal, and proposed that either Anson's sea lion, or perhaps a sea elephant would satisfactorily fill the role. These, he pointed out, had been known to drift northwards from the Antarctic Ocean on ice floes, to be consigned eventually to the inhospitable Atlantic by the melting away of their raft. He believed that the *Daedalus* animal was one of these larger species of seals, who had first approached the ship in the desperate hope of finding a new headquarters from which to conduct its daily search for food. Being disappointed in this aim it had swum on to an inevitable death by exhaustion and drowning

Captain M'Quhae, a naval captain of long standing, might well have replied to this suggestion that he knew a seal when he saw one. In fact he exercised admirable restraint, contenting himself with a reaffirmation of the points he had previously made, especially that there was at least 60 feet of the animal visible *à fleur d'eau*. As the largest recorded specimen of a bull elephant seal is well under 25 feet long, the seal hypothesis cannot now be regarded as one of Owen's happiest inspirations.

As time went on several other 'explanations' were given, but all of them seemed rather less likely than the phenomenon they set out to explain – namely, that an unknown animal had actually been seen. F. T. Bullen in *Creatures of the Sea* (1904) said that the creature was probably a rorqual, a proposal implying a degree of incompetent observation by Captain M'Quhae and his officers that even Professor Owen had not dared to suggest. Henry Lee in *Sea Monsters Unmasked* (1884) proposed a giant calamary, or squid, and reproduced an intriguing picture to show how the illusion might have come

Lee's explanation of the Daedalus sea serpent as a giant squid. From *Sea Monsters Unmasked* (1884)

about. But squids progress by a series of jerks, not in the even manner that apparently characterized the *Daedalus* animal. Also, as Lee himself pointed out, the witnesses had claimed to be so close to the creature that the eye, mouth, nostril and other details of the head could be easily distinguished.

Despite the various explanations that have been put forward there seems little question that the *Daedalus* sea serpent must still be regarded as an unexplained mystery. But that seals, squids, whales or porpoises could account for a large number of sea serpent reports, I do not doubt for an instant. For example, in a letter published in the *Illustrated London News* on April 14th 1848 a gentleman signing himself 'A Naval Officer' records an encounter with a 'sea-serpent' in the North Atlantic off Oporto. The vessel concerned was H.M.S. *Plumper*, and the creature, which was seen on the morning of December 31st 1848 by several members of the crew, was moving at about 2 knots. It was long and black with a sharp head which it carried between 6 and 8 feet above the water. The features were apparently not distinguishable, but about 20 feet of its back were exposed to view upon which a mane-like growth kept washing about as it moved through the sea. The writer adds: 'The officers and men who saw it, and who have served in parts of the world adjacent to the whale and seal fisheries, and have seen them in the water, declare they have neither seen nor heard of any creature bearing the slightest resemblance to the one we saw.'

Now here is an instance for which there is no need whatever to postulate the existence of an unknown animal, whether it be sea serpent or anything else. The account, together with a drawing which accompanied it, suggests that this creature was almost certainly a giant squid drifting lazily on the surface.

The very existence of giant squids was regarded as an old wives' tale until the second half of the nineteenth century, and as they have frequently been put forward as explanations of sea serpents a few details about them may not be out of place. The two most familiar species are known to scientists as *Architeuthis princeps* and *Architeuthis harveyi*, and there are now numerous records of their appearance in the North Atlantic. They are gigantic marine invertebrates of the phylum Cephalopoda, or 'head-feet', and are related not only to the octopus, but also, surprisingly enough, to the tiny snails and clams. They have long tubular bodies measuring between 10 and 15 feet long, and the mouth, with its hooked beak, is surrounded by ten snake-like tentacles. Two of these are considerably larger than the rest and may measure on occasion between 40 and 50 feet, making the total length of the creature about 65 feet, or even more. Their usual habitat is the deep sea, but on the rare occasions that they rise to the surface their appearance could easily account for the animal seen by the crew of the *Plumper*. The end of the body furthest from the head comes to a sharp point equipped with two lobes, or fins, that would explain in this, and many other sea serpent stories, the alleged existence of a 'mane'. When one takes these facts into account, and remembers that in 1849 the giant squid was itself a creature of rumour and legend, it is not difficult to see how easily a mistake could have been made.

An error of a somewhat similar kind was probably made by the captain and crew of the barque *Pauline* in 1875, when they described a titanic battle between a sea serpent and a whale off the north-east coast of Brazil. This episode was reported as follows in the *Illustrated London News* of November 20th 1875:

Captain Drevar, of the barque 'Pauline', bound with coals for Her Majesty's naval stores at Zanzibar, when in lat. 5 deg. 13 min. S., long, 35 deg. W., on July 8 last, observed three very large sperm whales, and one of them was gripped round the body with two turns, by what appeared to be a huge serpent. Its back was of a darkish brown and its belly white, with an immense head and mouth, the latter always open; the head and tail had a length beyond the coils about 30 ft; its girth was about 8 ft. or 9 ft. Using its extremities as levers, the serpent whirled its victim round and round for about fifteen minutes, and then suddenly dragged the whale down to the bottom, head first. The other two whales, after attempting to release their companion, swam away upon its descent, exhibiting signs of the greatest terror.

Alleged fight between a sea serpent and a sperm whale, seen from the barque
Pauline, July 8th 1875
From *The Illustrated London News*, November 20th 1875

Despite the fact that Captain Drevar made a desposition before the stipendiary magistrate of Liverpool, there is little doubt that what he really witnessed was a battle between a sperm whale and a giant squid. That such struggles take place is proved by the remains of giant squids, including huge beaks and tentacles, being frequently found in the stomachs of whales. There are two photographs published in *The Depths of the Sea* by Sir John Murray and Dr Johan Hjort showing the skin of a sperm whale scored with the marks of squid suckers measuring nearly an inch across. The coils of the 'sea serpent' wrapped around the *Pauline's* whale were almost certainly the tentacles of a giant squid, who far from being the victor in the battle was probably carried below the surface and devoured.

These two instances show how honest observers may easily be led through lack of zoological knowledge into making major errors of identification. Such, however, cannot be said of the next important appearance of the sea serpent, which now for the first time revealed itself to two expert naturalists who were actually taking part in a scientific expedition. The episode took place in the winter of 1905 off the north-east coast of Brazil, not far from the scene of the *Pauline's* dramatic battle. It was witnessed from the Earl of Crawford's yacht *Valhalla*, which had left England in November 1905 for a seven months' winter cruise to the South Atlantic and Indian Oceans for the purposes of scientific research. The witnesses' names were E. G. B. Meade-Waldo, and Michael J. Nicoll – the former being a Member of Council of the Zoological Society of London, the latter a Fellow – and their extraordinary experience formed the subject of a paper communicated to the Society at its Scientific Meeting on June 19th 1906. Here is the story in Meade-Waldo's own words:

On Dec. 7th 1905, at 10.15 A.M., I was on the poop of the 'Valhalla' with Mr Nicoll, when he drew my attention to an object in the sea about 100 yards from the yacht; he said: 'Is that the fin of a great fish?' I looked and immediately saw a large fin or frill sticking out of the water, dark seaweed-brown in colour, somewhat crinkled at the edge. It was apparently about 6 feet in length and projected from 18 inches to 2 feet from the water. I could see, under the water to the rear of the frill, the shape of a considerable body. I got my field-glasses on to it (a powerful pair of Goerz Triëder), and almost as soon as I had them on the frill, a great head and neck rose out of the water in front of the frill; the neck did not touch the frill in the water, but came out of the water in *front* of it, at a distance of certainly not less than 18 inches, probably more. The neck appeared about the thickness of a slight man's body, and from 7 to 8 feet was out of the water; head and neck were all about the same thickness. The head had a very turtle-like appearance, as had also the eye. I could see the line of the mouth, but we were sailing pretty fast, and quickly drew away from the object, which was going very slowly. It moved its neck from side to side in a peculiar manner: the colour of the head and neck was dark brown above, and whitish below – almost white, I think. . . . Since I saw this creature I consider on reflection that it was probably considerably larger than it appeared at first, as I proved that objects, the size with which I was well acquainted, appear very much smaller than they really are when seen on the ocean at a similar distance with nothing to compare them with.

The animal seen from the yacht *Valhalla*, December 7th 1905. From the
Proceedings of the Zoological Society of London (1906)

Michael Nicoll's report to the Zoological Society added little to that already given by Meade-Waldo, except that the head and neck, which he estimated as being about 6 feet long, lashed up the water with a curious wriggling movement. He also compared the fin to a gigantic piece of ribbon seaweed, and added that every now and then it disappeared entirely below the surface. But in his book *Three Voyages of a Naturalist* (1908) Nicoll was prepared to go somewhat further. The following observation strikes me as particularly interesting: 'I feel sure', he says, 'that it was not a reptile that we saw, but a mammal. It is, of course, impossible to be certain of this, but the general appearance of the creature, especially the soft, almost rubber-like fin, give one this impression.'

I shall shortly come back to this possibility, and to the

suggestion made by the late Dr A. C. Oudemans, Director of
the Royal Zoological Gardens at the Hague, that all alleged
'sea serpents' may in fact be mammals. In the meantime, however, mention must be made of two other reports, which although
less authoratively documented than the foregoing, may yet
help to throw some light on the problem. The first antedates the
Valhalla incident by twelve years, having taken place in the
North Atlantic off the coast of French West Africa in 1893.
On December 4th of that year the Natal line steamer *Umfuli*,
Captain R. J. Cringle, was passing down the west coast of
Africa heading for the Cape of Good Hope, when at 5.30 p.m.
about 400 to 500 yards away on the starboard side a large
creature with a serpentine head and neck rose from the sea. It
was seen not only by Captain Cringle, but by several passengers
and members of the crew. The sea was calm and the weather
clear, so there was virtually no possibility of an optical illusion.
The mate, Mr C. A. W. Powell, logged the occurrence as
follows:

5.30. Sighted and passed about 500 yards from ship a Monster
Fish of the Serpent shape, about 80 ft. long with slimy skin and short
fins at about 20 feet apart on the back and in cir. about the dimensions of a full sized whale. I distinctly saw the fish's mouth open
and shut with my glasses. The jaws appeared to me about 7 feet
long with large teeth. In shape it was just like a Conger Eel.

Captain Cringle said later that the animal was rushing
through the sea at great speed and was throwing water from its
breast as a vessel throws water from her bows. The head and
neck were about 15 feet long and sprang from a massive body
with three slight but clearly discernible humps. He turned the
ship round and followed it, approaching much nearer than he
was at first, but had to give up the chase after twenty minutes
for the sun was setting and the light gone.

Commander Rupert T. Gould, who spent many years
investigating sea serpent reports and had an interesting cor-
respondence with Captain Cringle on the *Umfuli* episode,
regards this story as one of the creature's most convincing
appearances. We cannot perhaps go all the way with him when
he suggests that the *Umfuli* appearance alone ought to prove
the existence of the animal, but Captain Cringle's account is

certainly difficult to explain away on any other hypothesis. Moreover, the description given by the witnesses on board the *Umfuli* is not incompatible with several other classic sea serpent reports, including that of the *Daedalus*, while there is certainly at least a family resemblance to the creature seen a few years later from the *Valhalla*.

I come now to one of the most famous and, I regret to say, one of the most suspect, of the creature's many visitations. I refer to the appearance in Scotland in the summer of 1933 of the notorious Loch Ness monster. This alleged sea serpent received greater publicity than any previous specimen of the genus. Reported in a small way in the *Northern Chronicle* and the *Inverness Courier* during the summer months, it had become by October a major international sensation. Mr Bertram Mills offered £20,000 to anyone who would deliver the monster alive to his circus, while the New York Zoological Society soon put up £5,000 as a similar inducement. There were articles, lectures, and broadcast talks, and the hotels of Inverness were crammed with representatives not only of the British Press but of such unlikely journals as the *Osaka Moinichi* and the *Tokyo Nichinchi*. One enthusiast even offered, in the columns of the *Glasgow News*, to swim across the loch, 'as a challenge to the Monster', and a *Daily Mail* expedition triumphantly found examples of its spoor, which it later transpired had been laid down by some wag with an ashtray made from a dried hippopotamus hoof. Finally in June 1934 the creature reached the pinnacle of its fame with the publication of a 228 page book by Commander Gould entirely devoted to its doings. No one sea serpent had ever received such an honour before.

Although the evidence in Goulds' book is most painstakingly compiled, it is also, I am afraid, extremely unconvincing. The only fact to emerge from many of the reports is that a number of black humps were seen floating or moving at various speeds along the surface of the Loch. Their number ranged from one to eight, and the witnesses agreed that they must belong to some large animal moving just out of sight below the water. Some people also claimed to have seen a long serpentine neck and small head emerge from the Loch, which turned slowly from side to side as if spying out the land before sinking once more beneath the surface. This was sometimes seen alone and sometimes in association with the mysterious humps described above.

The really classic description, however, is probably that provided by Mr and Mrs G. Spicer who claimed actually to have seen the monster on dry land. On July 22nd 1933 they were motoring round the loch in broad daylight when a most extraordinary animal crossed the road in front of their car. It had a thick body without any sign of legs, and a long neck which undulated up and down 'in the manner of a scenic

The Loch Ness monster, as reported by Mr and Mrs Spicer. From R. T. Gould's *The Case for the Sea-Serpent*

railway'. The colour of its body was grey, like a dirty elephant or a rhinoceros, and it moved in a series of jerks. On the fore-part of its back it appeared to be carrying a small lamb, young deer, or other animal of indeterminate species. The head was not observed, but Mr Spicer likened the general effect of this astonishing apparition to a huge snail with a long neck.

Excusably Mr Spicer's story was at first regarded as a hoax, but it was confirmed in startling fashion by a Mr Arthur Grant of Edinburgh, who some six months later claimed that an animal closely resembling Mr Spicer's had loped across the road in front of his motor bicycle. Despite the fact that this episode occurred at night, the moon was high and he was there-fore more fortunate than Mr Spicer in being able to make out the details of the head. This was like that of an eel with large eyes set high up towards the crown. He also observed that the animal had strong front flippers and a rounded tail, It was black, about 18 feet in length, and moved by arching its back on front and hind flippers alternately.

This description, combined with that of Mr Spicer and of those witnesses who had seen the animal in the water, gives us such a clear and unmistakable picture of one of the Phocidae, or true seals, that it seems almost impossible that the 'Loch Ness monster' could have deceived the public for so long. This seal, probably a large specimen of the common seal, *Phoca vitulina* – the same species incidentally which, transformed into a mermaid, may have beguiled Mr Munro off the coast of Caithness –' must have entered the loch by way of the river Ness sometime in the spring of 1933. After an eventful stay of nearly a year it probably returned to the Firth of Beauly and thence to the open sea by the same route. Admittedly some observers of the monster report it to have been much larger than the usual run of seals, and there are several slightly different versions of its colour and shape; in my opinion, however, there is not one of these that cannot be accounted for by tricks of light or faulty estimation of measurements. It is also most probable that some of the reports refer not to the seal at all, but to other mammals such as otters, or even to water birds or floating tree trunks, which untrained and expectant witnesses might easily transform into mysterious and sinister forms.

Reluctantly then, I feel we must abandon the Loch Ness monster's claim to be a genuine sea serpent. To insist on its *bona fides* would be to overstate a case which in other directions there is considerable evidence to support. Although, as was suggested earlier, squids and other known but unrecognized animals can account for many alleged appearances of the sea serpent, they cannot account for all. What explanation are we to give, for instance, of the New England serpent or the creatures seen from the *Daedalus*, the *Umfuli*, and the *Valhalla?* These and other genuinely inexplicable incidents were considered at some length by Dr A. C. Oudemans, who synthesized the various descriptions and produced an imaginary composite animal which, if it existed, would cover all the reports. This creature, depicted opposite, had much to commend it, but I cannot help feeling that Dr Oudemans' attempt to make it account for nearly every appearance of the sea serpent, no matter how contradictory the evidence, is a little naïve. For instance he was obviously troubled by the fact that several of the reports of large sea serpents speak of a mane, frill or dorsal fin, whereas others do not. To explain this anomaly he writes: 'In my opinion large individuals are males, and must have a mane, or at one time have had one. The probability exists that they lose the greater part of their mane at a certain age, or that they were moulting when they were seen; which would account for the fact that in some large individuals no mane was observed.' In thus attempting to make the best of all possible worlds, I feel that Dr Oudemans puts too much strain upon our credulity.

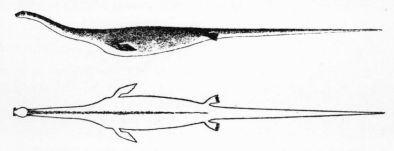

Oudemans' composite sea serpent. From *The Great Sea Serpent* (1892)

Another popular explanation of the sea serpent is that it may be a survival of one of the great sea reptiles of the Mesozoic Age. This was a time in Earth history when the world was completely dominated by reptiles – dinosaurs on the land, pterosaurs in the air, and great monsters known as ichthyosaurs, plesiosaurs and mosasaurs in the sea. The nineteenth century naturalist Philip Gosse was a great supporter of the plesiosaur theory, and in the first volume of *The Romance of Natural History* he examines the evidence for and against it in some detail. He comes to the conclusion that although the Mesozoic Age ended tens of millions of years ago, and there was therefore little likelihood that a plesiosaur genus of that time had existed unchanged down to the present day, there was no *a priori* reason why one of the descendants of the group should not have survived and attained to the gigantic proportions often ascribed to the sea serpent. This possibility has recently been supported by the discovery of crossopterygian fish off south-east Africa which have survived almost unchanged from even earlier times.

But although there is nothing intrinsically impossible in the theory, there is much to be said for a less extreme view. In the first place, it seems to me that several explanations of the sea serpent have fallen down because they have attempted to find one genus of animals that will account for all the appearances. We have already quoted suggestions that seals, giant squids and other animals have almost certainly played a part in some versions of the story, and that tree trunks and other floating objects have accounted for many others. It seems very probable that some at least of the reports that have not yet been explained may have had an equally prosaic origin.

For example, in his recent book *Living Fossils*, Dr Maurice Burton has pointed out two facts that may provide an explanation of the New England sea serpent, and others which have been characterized by a series of humps showing above the water line. He first reminds us that in recent years eel larvae 3 feet long have been discovered in the sea. Working on the comparative sizes of the larvae and adults in eels of normal size he points out that there is no reason why the giant larvae, when full grown, should not reach a length of 36 feet. He next describes some observations of eels in the Aquarium at the London Zoo, particularly of a large conger which suddenly rose to the top of the tank, turned on its side, and vigorously undulated its body, causing a violent commotion in the water and showing a row of humps above the surface. Such a performance, if carried out by a really large eel, would give an excellent approximation to the appearance of the New England sea serpent and several others of its kind.

Yet, ingenious as this explanation is, we must still admit that a number of apparently inexplicable cases remain. For example, the *Daedalus* serpent showed no sign of humps, and we must recall Captain M'Quhae's words, that no visible portion of its body was used in propelling it through the water, either by vertical or horizontal undulation. Nor is there any justification for the view that this animal may have been a seal. Despite the fact that its movements suggest propulsion by seal-like flippers or paddles below the water line, it was far larger than any species of seal yet known to science. We must also admit

44

2a The sea serpent, on the plesiosaur hypothesis favoured by Philip Gosse. From Gosse's *Romance of Natural History* (1860)

2b The extinct whale *Zeuglodon* as it probably appeared in life.
Reconstruction by Maurice Wilson

that such creatures as that seen from the yacht *Valhalla*, with its serpentine head and neck and crinkled fin, cannot possibly be explained by reference to any familiar creature.

For such appearances it certainly seems possible – and no more than that can be said – that we may have to invoke the existence of a previously unknown animal. Accepting this possibility, to what natural class is it most likely to belong?

The traditional view is that it is a serpent, a member of the class Reptilia, and in all probability a survival of the world of over 70 million years ago. As mentioned above, I cannot help feeling that this assumption is too extreme. Far more plausible is the suggestion that the 'sea serpent', if it really exists, may be a gigantic aquatic mammal related either to the whales or to the seals, walruses and sea elephants. Oudemans favoured the latter view and devoted 74 pages of his book *The Great Sea Serpent* to a full account of its natural history, including its form, shape, habits, and sexual differences, as well as whole sections devoted to its physiological and even its psychological character. This, for an animal whose very existence is still largely in doubt, seems certainly to be going too far. Yet the mammalian theory as such has two strong points in its favour. Firstly, the mane which is constantly ascribed to sea serpents would, to say the least of it, be an unlikely appendage in an aquatic reptile. And secondly, a warm blooded mammal would be far more likely than a reptile to survive in the cold waters of the North Atlantic where so many sea serpent stories have originated.

Personally, rather than the theory of a huge, seal-like animal, I would suggest that at least some of the appearances could be accounted for by an ancient and as yet undiscovered species of whale. For example, the whale known as *Zeuglodon* or *Basilosaurus*, whose fossil remains are well known in the Tertiary rocks and were put to such good use by Dr Koch, would be a very suitable animal to cast in the role of sea serpent. It was a huge creature with a slim and greatly elongated body sometimes measuring over 70 feet long. The skull was long and low and the animal was propelled by a single pair of fins or flappers at the forward end. Smaller members of the group are already known to have survived until at least the beginning of the Miocene Epoch just over 30 million years ago, and there is certainly no reason why some of their larger relations may not even now linger in the seas. The possibility is certainly more likely than that a race of Mesozoic plesiosaurs has survived for nearly 100 million years, especially when one remembers that every other great reptile of the Age has become extinct.

To sum up, the age-long enigma of the great sea serpent is still unsolved. Although many of its visitations can be accounted for in terms of seals, giant squids, sharks, and other sea creatures that are by no means unfamiliar, a central core of mystery remains. Whether the sea serpent will ever be identified with a giant ocean reptile surviving from the age of the dinosaurs, or a primitive whale from the early part of the Tertiary Period, remains to be seen. Meanwhile it still justifies the romantic title bestowed upon it nearly a century ago by Philip Gosse – the Great Unknown of the seas.

CHAPTER THREE

The Kraken and other Sea Monsters

Amongst the many great things which are in the ocean, and concealed from our eyes, or only presented to our view for a few minutes, is the Kraken. This creature is the largest and most surprizing of all the animal creation, and consequently well deserves such an account as the nature of the thing, according to the Creator's wise ordinance, will admit of.

ERIK PONTOPPIDAN: *Natural History of Norway* (1755)

Below the thunders of the upper deep;
Far, far beneath in the abysmal sea,
His ancient, dreamless, uninvaded sleep
The Kraken sleepeth: faintest sunlights flee
About his shadowy sides: above him swell
Huge sponges of millennial growth and height;
And far away into the sickly light,
From many a wondrous grot and secret cell
Unnumber'd and enormous polypi
Winnow with giant arms the slumbering green.
There hath he lain for ages and will lie
Battening upon huge seaworms in his sleep,
Until the latter fire shall heat the deep;
Then once by man and angels to be seen,
In roaring he shall rise and on the surface die.

TENNYSON: *The Kraken*

BEFORE we leave the sea altogether, a few words must be said about three more of its legendary inmates – the kraken, the hydra and that fascinating creature known variously as the sea monk and the sea bonze. None of these has had quite such a long or colourful history as the mermaid or the sea serpent, but they are a good example of the way legends are built up from a mixture of superstition and scientific fact. We will begin with the Norwegian kraken, or kraxen, which forces itself on our attention by its size alone.

Erik Pontoppidan, in the quotation heading this chapter, refers to the kraken as 'the largest and most surprizing of all the animal creation' – a view from which we can hardly dissent when we are told that a good sized specimen measured about a mile and a half in circumference. In fact the kraken was so huge that sailors often mistook it for an island – an error which led on occasion to disastrous results. Thus in the works of several Renaissance naturalists, including the famous Olaus Magnus, Archbishop of Upsala, sailors have been known to land on one of these 'islands', and light fires and settle down for the night. Understandably the kraken in such circumstances resented having its back used as a hearth and would sink beneath the waves, carrying the sailors with him.

But the kraken on the whole was a harmless creature and seems, moreover, to have had a healthy respect for the church. A story is told of how a bishop, voyaging home to his own country from foreign parts, noticed near the shore an island which he knew had not been there before. Being anxious to consecrate this new land in the name of God he had himself rowed across to it, erected an altar and held a full Mass. Of course the island was really a kraken, and it is pleasant to be able to record that it waited respectfully till the ceremony was over and the bishop safely back in his boat before it slowly sank from sight.

Norwegian fishermen had good reason to be grateful to the kraken for its help in bringing them good catches. Pontoppidan writes:

Our fishermen unanimously affirm, and without the least variation in their accounts, that when they row out several miles to sea, particularly in the hot Summer days, and by their situations (which they know by taking a view of certain points of land) expect to find 80 or 100 fathoms water, it often happens that they do not find above 20 or 30, and sometimes less. At these places they generally find the greatest plenty of Fish, especially Cod and Ling. Their lines, they say, are no sooner out than they may draw them up with the hooks all full of Fish; by this they judge that the Kraken is at the bottom. . . .

There are sometimes twenty boats or more got together, and throwing out their lines at a moderate distance from each other; and the only thing they then have to observe is whether the depth continues the same (which they know by their lines), or whether it grows shallower by their seeming to have less water. If this last be the case, they find that the Kraken is raising himself nearer the surface, and then it is not time for them to stay any longer; they immediately leave off fishing, take to their oars, and get away as fast as they can. . . .

This anxiety of the fishermen to put a healthy distance between themselves and the emerging kraken shows that their gratitude was rightly tempered with respect. Pontoppidan's own comment is at once reassuring and slightly sinister. 'The Kraken has never been known to do any great harm', he says, 'except they have taken away the lives of those who consequently could not bring the tidings.'

In one version of the legend it is said that only two kraken exist. These were created at the beginning of the world and will finally appear on the surface and die when it comes to an end. That this is not the general view is shown by Pontoppidan's story of a kraken ('perhaps a young and careless one') which became trapped among the rocks near Frederikstad in the diocese of Aggerhuus. It died before it could regain the sea, and the narrow channel at that point was made almost impassable by the intolerable stench.

So much, then, for the Scandinavian aspects of the legend. But we have not so far quoted any passage that might give us a clue as to what the kraken actually is. For this we will go back to much earlier times – to Pliny's *Natural History* in fact – where there is a graphic description of an animal which seems certainly to have played some part in the Kraken's ancestry.

Pliny quotes Trebius Niger, a follower of the Roman proconsul on Boetica, concerning an enormous monster with massive arms that emerged from the sea each night to steal salted tunny from the curing ponds and cisterns at Rocadillo in Spain. In the words of Philemon Holland's translation: 'hee practised so long, that in the end he gat himselfe the anger and displeasure of the masters and keepers of the said ponds and cisterns, with his continuall and immeasurable filching.' The monster even used a tree to scale the fence that had been erected round the depot in an effort to keep it out.

Finally one night the creature was cornered by dogs on its journey between the depot and the sea. After a tremendous battle it was killed, and its head was shown to the local pro-consul, Lucullus, 'for a wonder'. This was reputed to be as big as a 90 gallon cask, while its arms were 30 feet long and nearly two yards in circumference. The weight of the animal was 700 pounds.

Now here is an anecdote that must surely be based on fact, for although the size of the creature is somewhat exaggerated it has a strong likeness to two sea animals that in later times became well known. The first is the octopus and the second is the great mollusc we have already met in connection with the sea serpent, the giant squid. Octopuses are renowned for their ability to travel short distances on land, and giant squids, as Trebius himself pointed out, were frequently cast up on the coast of Spain. By combining the land travelling aptitude of the octopus with the immense size of the giant squid, it is easy to see how Pliny's marauder probably originated. Its identity is also confirmed by the description of its 'arms' or tentacles which, as in both squids and octopuses, were arranged round its mouth and were mistaken by Trebius for a beard.

But to come back to the kraken. What evidence is there that it also can be likened to an octopus or squid, and is therefore probably a descendant of Trebius Niger's ocean monster?

If the kraken's appearances in the role of an island were the only facts we had to go on, it would certainly be difficult to prove any connection. Fortunately, however, this is not the case. Pontoppidan has noted that when the kraken comes to the surface it is 'surrounded with something that floats and fluctuates like sea-weeds'. 'At last', he continues, 'several bright points or horns appear, which grow thicker and thicker the higher they rise above the surface of the water, and sometimes they stand up as high and as large as the masts of middle-sized vessels. It seems these are the creature's arms, and, it is said, if they were to lay hold of the largest man of war, they would pull it down to the bottom. . . . As this enormous Sea-animal in all probability may be reckon'd of the Polype, or of the Star-fish kind, it seems that the parts which are seen rising at its pleasure, and are called arms, are properly the tentacula, or feeling instruments. . .'

Pontoppidan was mistaken when he suggested that his animal might be classified with the starfishes, for both squids and octopuses belong to the natural group known as the Cephalopoda, or 'head-feet', while the starfish belong to the Echinodermata, or 'spiny skins' – two quite distinct animal phyla. But there is little doubt that he was right in his general identification. Of the two animals octopus and squid, it is the squid which, by reason of its great size and sudden kraken-like appearances on the surface of the water, seems to have played the greater part in the legend. At the same time there seems to be a good dash of octopus in the kraken's make up, especially when we think of such episodes as the death of the 'young and careless one' mentioned above. We can also perhaps detect the influence of tidal sand banks or shifting shoals in some aspects of the story. As with all legends we can mix these various ingredients according to taste, but the fact remains that the Norwegian kraken is related by many unmistakable likenesses to Pliny's marauding monster.

But this is not quite the end of the story. The legendary kraken might have been reduced to the by no means negligible proportions of a giant squid, but the more sensational aspects of the cephalopods as a group had not, apparently, been finally exploited. This was proved by the appearance on the scene of the French naturalist Denis de Montfort with an entirely new addition to their natural history. In his *Histoire Naturelle Générale et Particulière des Mollusques*, published in Paris between 1802 and 1805, he devotes a blood-curdling chapter to the doings of a creature which he refers to as the *poulpe colossal*. The high spot of his account is the story of how one of these creatures attacked a three-masted sailing ship off the coast of Angola and attempted to drag it to the bottom of the sea. This, he is certain, would have been its fate had not the crew saved themselves by a desperate counter-attack on its tentacles with knives and hatchets. Naturally enough the names of the participants in this dramatic encounter are not revealed, and the story, based on the slender evidence of a picture in the church of St. Thomas at St. Malo, is obviously apocryphal. Nevertheless it raised such widespread interest that de Montfort was encouraged to even higher flights of fancy, 'If my entangled ship is accepted', he is reported to have said, 'I will make my *poulpe colossal* overthrow a whole fleet'. This, with a slight variation in genus, he proceeded to do. He refers to the occasion when six French ships were captured by Admiral Rodney in the West Indies on April 12th 1782 and were being convoyed to port by four British men of war. On the very night of the battle all ten of these ships were engulfed in such mysterious circumstances that the only explanation could have been, in his opinion, an onslaught by giant cuttle-

De Montfort's 'poulpe colossal'. From Sonnini's edition of Buffon's *Natural History* (Vol. 88, 1802)

fishes. Unfortunately the facts as recorded by the British Admiralty were quite otherwise, and after desperate efforts to redeem his reputation de Montfort is said to have abandoned natural history for a career of crime and to have died eventually in the galleys.

An account of one of the earliest authentic meetings with a giant squid was communicated to the Academy of Sciences in Paris in 1861 by two of its members, M. Flourens and M. Moquin-Tandon, and was based on a report by Lieutenant Bouyer, commander of the French sloop *Alecton*, to the Ministre de la Marine, and a letter from M. Sabin Berthelot, French consul in the Canaries. I will let Lieutenant Bouyer's report speak for itself:

Sainte-Croix de Ténériffe.
Alecton, 2nd. Dec. 1861.

Monsieur le Ministre,

I have the honour to inform your Excellency that I dropped anchor at Teneriffe on December 1st at 8 a.m.

In my passage from Cadiz to Teneriffe, that is, between November 27th and December 1st, the weather was extremely favourable; also, by using the sail and reducing power on the engines – in other words by economizing as far as possible in fuel – I was able at times to reduce consumption to six tons per day, travelling at 7 to 8 knots, with a moderate north-easterly breeze.

The voyage was distinguished by a singular incident. On November 30th, 100 miles N.E. of Teneriffe, at 2 p.m., we encountered a monstrous animal which I recognized as the *Poulpe géant* whose existence has been so much disputed and now seems to be relegated to the realms of myth.

Finding myself in the presence of one of these extraordinary beings which the Ocean throws up periodically from its depths as if in open defiance of scientific opinion, I decided to study it at close quarters, and if possible to catch it.

Unfortunately we were taking a heavy swell on the beam which caused the *Alecton* to roll violently, and prevented easy manoeuvre. In addition the animal itself, although almost always *à fleur d'eau*, kept changing its position with a sort of intelligence, and seemed anxious to give the ship a wide berth.

After a number of approaches which only allowed us to get home a dozen or so bullets, I succeeded in drawing sufficiently close to harpoon it and encircle it with a running noose. We were just on the point of getting more ropes round it when a violent lunge by the animal broke the harpoon; the part of the tail encircled by the noose broke away and we hauled on board only a fragment weighing about forty pounds.

We saw the creature at close enough range to be able to give an exact description of it. It was in fact the giant calamary, but the shape of the tail suggested it belonged to a species not yet described. The body seemed to measure about 15 to 18 feet in length. The head had a parrot-like beak surrounded by eight arms between 5 and 6 feet long. In aspect it was quite appalling; brick red in colour, shapeless and slimy, its form repulsive and terrible.

The officers and men asked me to lower a boat so that the animal could once again be roped and brought finally on board. They might have succeeded in doing this, but I was afraid that in such a hand to hand struggle with the monster, it might capsize the boat with its long tentacles, and perhaps use these formidable whip-like weapons, armed with suckers and charged with electricity, to strangle several of my sailors.

I did not feel that I ought to endanger the lives of my men simply for the sake of curiosity, even though of a scientific kind; and in spite of the excitement produced by such a chase, I felt I must abandon the wounded animal, which by a sort of instinct seemed carefully to avoid the ship, diving backwards and forwards beneath the keel each time we tried to make a new approach.

I must beg Your Excellency to excuse the long and detailed account into which I have entered. I thought it would be not without value to provide some authentic information concerning this *force de mer*, as one famous writer calls it. I felt that we whose profession sometimes allows us glimpses of the strange mysteries of the Ocean, had a duty to pass on our truthful observations, and entrust them to other more expert hands. . . .

Except for the fact that Lieutenant Bouyer miscounted the arms of the monster (a squid normally has ten tentacles, but in this case two may have been bitten off in combat with a sperm whale), and wrongly attributed to them an electric charge, his report gives an excellent picture of the size and appearance of one of these formidable giant squids – the genuine krakens of natural history. Since the *Alecton* episode the giant squid has become comparatively well known. One specimen, captured in 1877 in Trinity Bay, Newfoundland, was preserved in brine and exhibited in the New York Aquarium, while now nearly every natural history museum has on display a model giant squid and sections of the beak and tentacles. Thus the

3a The kraken, as seen by the eye of imagination. From Gibson's *Monsters of the Sea* (1887)

b The 'poulpe géant' encountered by the French sloop *Alecton* on November 30th 1861. *Redrawn by Maurice Wilson after a contemporary engraving*

kraken has at last ended its fabulous career correctly labelled *Architeuthis princeps.*

For our second mystery animal of the sea we have to go back even further than Pliny – to the time in fact of the Homeric myths of more than twenty-five centuries ago. The Lernean hydra is not actually mentioned by Homer, but its destruction was the second of the twelve famous 'labours of Hercules', who was the most notorious of the Greek heroes, and whose exploits formed one of the main themes of classical mythology. I purposely describe Hercules as notorious rather than famous, for contrary to popular belief he seems to have been a particularly unattractive specimen of manhood. He represented the triumph of brawn over brain to an extent that even the muscle-bound superman of the modern strip cartoon has hardly been able to equal.

Having killed his wife, Megara, and his three sons in a fit of madness, one of his few redeeming acts was to seek absolution from the oracle at Delphi. The oracle instructed him to enter the service of one Eurystheus, who was to set him a number of penitential tasks. Not the least formidable of these was to slay the powerful monster known as the hydra, the offspring of Typhon and Echidna, which used to ravage the country of Lerna, near Argos. The hydra, which dwelt in a swamp near the well of Amymone, was reputed to have nine heads, the middle one of which was immortal. Hercules sought out the monster and attacked it, but each time he lopped off one of its heads two more grew in its place. Finally, with the help of his faithful servant and companion Iolaus, he succeeded in destroying eight of the heads by burning them away, and buried the ninth or immortal one under a great stone. Unfortunately after all this exertion Eurystheus decided that this particular achievement would not count towards the penance as Iolaus had helped his master to accomplish it.

It may seem rather ambitious to seek for a real animal behind the legend of the hydra, but a moment's thought will show us what it is. There is in the vicinity of Greece even today an eight 'headed' monster which answers the description very well – the octopus. The eight heads are of course represented by the creature's tentacles, the immortal head by the real head of the animal which the tentacles surround.

But, we may ask, what of the legendary belief that if any of the heads was lopped off, two more would grow in its place? Even this seemingly fanciful idea is soundly rooted in natural history. The octopus, unlike the giant squid, is capable of growing new tentacles if the original ones are amputated by its predatory foes. Sometimes when octopuses are caught they are found to have one or more tentacles shorter than the rest, and from these stumps there often project thin whip-like growths about the thickness of a pencil which represent the first stage in the formation of new arms. This well verified scientific fact was obviously the starting point for the legendary hydra's power of repairing and even duplicating its own 'heads'.

That the ancients were familiar with the octopus is proved by the excavations carried out by Dr Schliemann at Mycenae in 1876. Here numerous gold ornaments were found inscribed with excellent representations of the octopus, showing the head, body, eight tentacles, and sometimes even the suckers. A marble

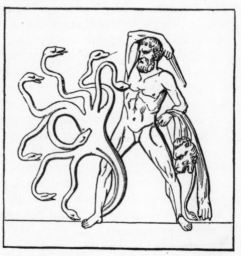

Hercules killing the Hydra. From a marble
tablet in the Vatican

tablet in the Vatican showing Hercules killing a most octopus-like hydra proves that the identification of the two animals is by no means a new discovery. By the Renaissance, however, the connection between them had largely been lost. None of the naturalists of the time, who in any case acquired their knowledge from books rather than direct observation of nature, could make up their minds whether the hydra was a real or imaginary animal. Edward Topsell reproduces a popular contemporary woodcut of the hydra in his *Historie of Serpents* (1608) with the comment: 'that there shold be such a serpent with seaven heads, I think it unpossible'. But others were equally convinced of its reality, and it vied with the dragon, the leviathan and the behemoth as a subject of popular controversy. It was not until Victor Hugo's *Toilers of the Sea* had stimulated new interest in the octopus and its habits that its close connection with the hydra legend was finally established.

Although less lethal than its legendary counterpart the real 'hydra' is by no means unimpressive. The largest octopus known is *Octopus apollyon* with a diameter of over 25 feet, but this giant is confined to the North Pacific and would therefore never have been encountered by the ancient Greeks. The classical octopus would have been *Octopus vulgaris*, which is com-

M. Wilson.

Octopus vulgaris, the real hydra of natural history

mon in temperate waters and is not unknown round the coast of Britain. The British specimens are comparatively small and an octopus with tentacles more than 2 feet long is exceptional. But in the Mediterranean much larger examples occur. Some of these may have tentacles 4 feet long, making the animals' total diameter in the region of 10 feet. Such a specimen could be extremely dangerous even to such a reputedly husky individual as Hercules.

Mediterranean octopuses have taken their toll of human

victims through the ages and many lurid tales have been told. There is little doubt that some of these are true. For instance in the last century there was a well authenticated story of how a succession of French soldiers mysteriously disappeared while bathing off the Algerian coast. On one occasion a group of soldiers were bathing when one of their number screamed for help. Rushing to his aid, the others found that he was firmly gripped by four tentacles of a large octopus, the remaining tentacles anchoring the creature to a rock. They released him with difficulty and in revenge for the death of their former friends boiled the octopus alive and ate it.

There is a tendency nowadays to belittle the dangerous possibilities of an encounter with an octopus, and it is true that many incidents have been grossly exaggerated. On the other hand anyone who has felt the strength in the suckers of even the smallest octopus will not be likely to underestimate the risk. The specimens round the British coast are too small to inflict serious harm and are often quite friendly and playful, but among Mediterranean fishermen the occasional giant octopus, although less fearsome than the Lernean hydra, is treated with the respect that is its due.

I come now to the last of the supposedly legendary sea animals that I shall have space to consider in this chapter, the creature known in northern waters as the sea monk, and in the Far East as the sea bonze. Unlike the gigantic kraken and the formidable hydra, the sea monk of Norway was a comparatively small and inoffensive creature with more nuisance value than malice, which nevertheless had the power of whipping up sudden storms. It is described and illustrated by Guilielmus Rondeletius in his *Libri de Piscibus Marinis*, or Books of Sea Fishes, published in 1554, from which we learn that it derived its name from its monk's cowl and tonsured head; it had fins for arms, a human face – albeit of a somewhat crude kind – and its body ended in a sizeable tail.

A similar monster, 'much more wonderful than the one before', is also described. By its habit as well as its imposing manner this creature was deemed to be somewhat higher in the ecclesiastical scale than the sea monk, and hence became known as the sea bishop. The most famous representative of this interesting species had first been seen in Poland in 1531 and been taken at once to the king of that country. But the sea bishop does not appear to have been impressed by this honour, for it immediately made signs that it wished to return to the sea. Interested though he was, the king hardly liked to refuse

Sea monk and sea bishop. From Rondeletius's *Libri de Piscibus Marinis* (1554)

the pleasure of so exalted a personage and returned it to the coast where, we are told, it plunged immediately into the water as if glad to be rid of the vanity and pretentions of the court.

The Chinese sea monk, or sea bonze, seems to have been somewhat more formidable than his western counterpart. He was known as the *Hai Ho Shang*, or 'sea Buddhist priest' and was the terror of the fishermen along the South China coast. Not only did he have the power of raising storms, but would sometimes make direct attacks on the junks and capsize them. If this danger threatened, the most effective method of keeping the sea bonze at bay was by a ritual dance. On every junk there was at least one deck-hand who had been specially trained in the steps that would hold off the sea bonze, and these he would perform on the prow of the vessel, waving a stick decked with red streamers and accompanied by the rhythmic beating of a gong. Another protection against the *Hai Ho Shang* was the burning of feathers, for this was apparently a smell he could not abide, and he would be forced thereby to keep his distance.

Sometimes by chance the fishermen would haul up a whole shoal of young sea bonzes in their nets. A most moving scene would then ensue, for the terrified bonzes would fall on their knees and hold up their fins in prayer to their captors and beg for mercy. But unfortunately for them the fishermen never spared their lives; they felt that there were already enough adult sea bonzes to make life dangerous for them and to spare the young ones would be mere sentimentality.

Various explanations of the sea monk and sea bonze legends have been suggested, including yet once again the idea that they might be based on some kind of squid or cuttlefish. The reader, I fear, must already have become somewhat bored with this persistent creature, and I am therefore relieved to be able to say in this case that I consider the identification quite wrong. The fins and fish-like tail of the sea monk are not present in the cuttlefish, and a squid with a tonsured head is a phenomenon so far unknown to science. To my mind the most likely creatures to have originated the legend are those familiar fishes the skates and rays, whose smaller representatives are a popular feature of every sea water aquarium.

The skates and rays are closely related to the sharks but have become highly specialized for a less active life on the bottom of the sea. This has been achieved by a flattening of the body and an enormous expansion of the pectoral fins, which are fused with the sides of the trunk and of the head, giving the fish a square or rhomboidal shape like a kite. There are numerous varieties, most of which are found close inshore, but there are some deep sea forms in the tropics. The small rays seen in aquaria give no idea of the diversity of the group, which contains several gigantic forms such as the great devil fish, *Manta birostris*, which sometimes measures more than 20 feet across and may weigh nearly one and a half tons.

But how is it that the rays may have given rise to the legend of the sea monk and the sea bonze? I think here, as with all legends, we must consider evidence from several sources. In the first place there is the actual appearance of the creature. On the upper side of the body there is nothing particularly unusual to remark, but below there is a remarkable likeness to a grotesque human face. The corners of the mouth usually turn downward, giving the 'face' a most doleful and depressed

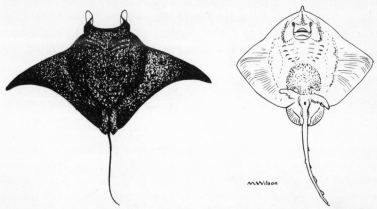

Manta birostris, the great devil fish (left), and the underside of a ray, showing its likeness to a human face

expression, while the spiracles above look extraordinarily like a pair of widely spaced eye-sockets. The effect is completed by the two groups of gill slits lying just below where the chin would be if rays had chins, and resembling sections of a kind of necklace or mayoral chain.

More evidence comes from the habits of some of the big rays found in tropical and sub-tropical seas. The great devil fish mentioned above is one of these, and is often seen on the surface with the tips of its wing-like fins curled right back out of the water. I have actually on two occasions seen a devil fish jump several feet into the air, a habit which is said to be quite common and is confirmed by J. R. Norman and F. C. Fraser in their book *Giant Fishes, Whales and Dolphins*. They quote here a description of the noise made by the fish when performing some of these jumps as being like a clap of thunder or the discharge of a cannon audible several miles away. The smaller species of devil fish belonging to the genus *Mobula* are also found in the Indian and Pacific Oceans, as well as in the Mediterranean and Atlantic, and in another significant passage Norman and Fraser write: 'When taken from the water they are said to make a musical bell-like barking noise, quite unlike the harsh grunt or bark made by some other rays.'

A gigantic creature with a man-like face, capable of a musical parody of speech, and producing awe inspiring sounds by jumping out of the water, surely takes us some way towards the identification of the sea bonze. But I have one further line of evidence to present before leaving the reader to make up his own mind. This concerns the strange creations known to

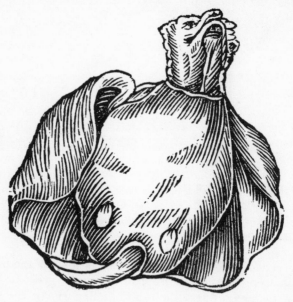

A Jenny Haniver made from a ray. From Aldrovandi's *Serpentum et Draconum Historiae* (1640)

naturalists and antiquarians as Jenny Hanivers. A Jenny Haniver is the body of a real animal changed by human skill and ingenuity into the semblance of an imaginary or legendary creature. These extraordinary objects were immensely popular in the sixteenth and seventeenth centuries, and were doubtless sold at a large profit either as curios or as true representations of dragons, basilisks and other mythical monsters. Conrad Gesner writes about them in his Historia *Animalium* and they are illustrated in several other natural histories of the time.

Now the interesting thing is that the real animal taken as

the basis of the great majority of Jenny Hanivers was none other than the skate or ray. The human 'face' made an admirable starting point for the craftsman's embellishments, and the enlarged pectoral fins could be cut and folded into an infinite variety of bizarre shapes. All that was then needed was to manipulate the mouth and other features of the face into a suitably grotesque expression, insert pieces of coloured glass for eyes, and dry the whole thing carefully so as to preserve its form. Jenny Hanivers of this kind are known chiefly from the west but it is almost certain that a similar art was practised in China and Japan. I have already described the artificial Japanese mermaids, made with such care and skill, and the east has always been a source of such macabre and startling oddities. We thus have all the ingredients for the growth of a similar legend in both parts of the world, and I personally believe that the parallel legends of the sea monk and the sea bonze grew up independently in this way. Combine a small dried Jenny Haniver, its pectoral fins folded into the semblance of a monk-like cloak, with stories of giant devil fish crashing like thunder on the surface of the water; add a few fishermen's tales of the strange sounds made by captured rays; bind the whole with equal parts of fear, wonder and superstition, and we have, I would submit, a reasonably likely explanation of the origin and natural history of the sea monk and the *Hai Ho Shang*.

CHAPTER FOUR

Dragons of East and West

Among all the kindes of Serpents, there is none comparable to the Dragon, or that affordeth and yeeldeth so much plentifull matter in history for the ample discovery of the nature thereof: and therefore heerein I must borrow more time . . . than peradventure the Reader would be willing to spare. . . . But I will strive to make the description pleasant, with variable history, seeing I may not avoyd the length heereof. . . .

EDWARD TOPSELL: *The Historie of Serpents* (1608)

The Dragon foul and fell –
  The unrevealable,
And hidden one, whose breath
Gives wind and fuel to the fires of Hell!

COLERIDGE: *Ne Plus Ultra*

THE most famous and universal of all animal legends relate to the unicorn and to the dragon. Of these the unicorn legend is the better documented, and several fine books, such as Odell Shepard's *The Lore of the Unicorn*, have been entirely devoted to unravelling its history. Dragons on the whole have fared less well. They appear in one form or another in the folk-lore of every country, but I have not been able to find any recent attempt to give a general picture of their natural history.

The main difficulty in dealing with the dragon legend is the immense volume and complexity of the evidence. There is not even general agreement on what a dragon looks like, let alone where it lives or how it behaves. There are land dragons and flying dragons, fire dragons and water dragons, and dragons who are fierce or timid, good or bad, affectionate or aloof. Thus any attempt to explain dragon lore must be extremely tentative and whatever theory is proposed, facts can always be produced that seem to contradict it.

In my view, the dragon legend, like that of the mermaid, arose in the first place as the result of a fundamental instinct in the mind of early man. I have stressed in my earlier book

A Guide to Earth History, how important a part was played in the development of the human consciousness by the forces of nature, and how the emotion which for want of a better term I called 'cosmic fear' lay at the base of primitive religion. This fear is quite different in kind from the alarm felt in the presence of physical danger, which was certainly felt as much by the food-gathering primate who was our ancestor as by every other animal. Cosmic fear is an emotion that so far as we know is unique to man. It is born of his consciousness of his own self, of his wonder at the mystery and immensity of the Universe around him, and above all of the terrifying realization of his own loneliness and insignificance.

When this new kind of awareness first dawned in the human mind it led to the creation of formal symbols to personify not only the seemingly hostile forces of nature but also the benevolent powers who would help man to combat them. In this way began the concepts of gods and goddesses, goblins, demons and evil spirits, and of such splendid and powerful mythological creatures as the dragon. It seems likely that the emotional stimulus that called each particular symbol into being was fundamental and universal, a part of the evolutionary pattern of man; but the symbol itself was bound to vary in different areas according to the experience and environment of its creators. Thus gods and religious beliefs differ greatly in different societies and in different parts of the world while, to take the particular case of the dragon, its description is always coloured by the various local animals who have been woven into the fabric of the legend. Thus there is not one dragon but many, and, as I shortly wish to suggest, the dragon of the east differs in many fundamental ways from the dragon of the west.

But to go back first of all to the original symbolism of the legend. What was it in the mind of early man that called this terrific symbol of the dragon into being, and why, with all its local variations, is it so universally recognizable? To answer these questions we must again invoke the concept of the sun god who, as we have already pointed out in connection with the natural history of mermaids, played such an important part in primitive belief. Even today children fear the dark and regard it as the abode of all evil things, while the sunset has not lost its emotional significance for man even when as too often

happens it forms the subject of somewhat crude and sentimen-
talized art. To our primitive ancestors the fear of darkness and
the emotional significance of sunset and the ensuing night were
more potent still. They lacked the scientific knowledge which
enables us to know that the dipping of the sun below the
horizon each evening is a natural and inevitable event, condi-
tioned by the astronomical processes which govern the Universe.
To them, when the sun set there was no guarantee that it
would ever rise again. They felt that the sun god had vanished
into the underworld, the abode of evil spirits and destructive
forces inimical to man. And while the sun god hid his face
and voyaged through the realms of darkness the first men
huddled round their camp fires for protection from the terror
that walks by night.

It is not difficult to see how a superstitious imagination
would build pictures of the inhabitants of that dark and
mysterious region beneath the ground. Surely there were devils
and giants there who might do harm to the sun god? Were
not great bones found sometimes in the ground and in the
entrances of caves? These must be the remains of the gigantic
denizens of the nether world, perhaps slain by the sun god on
his nightly journey. That such battles occurred was proved by
the thunder of his weapons and the great flashes of light that
seemed to rise sometimes from the ground during the hours of
darkness. But one day, perhaps, he himself might be killed by
some gigantic monster, and then there would be no more dawn.

Out of such dark reflections there grew up the idea of a race
of gigantic creatures living beneath the surface of the Earth.
These were the very type of the western dragon of later mythology, who was almost always hostile to man and was the
villain of a whole series of legendary battles with the forces of
light and life, represented in early times by the sun god and
later by the heroes of mythology and the militant saints of
the Christian church.

Restricting ourselves for the moment to these western
dragons, let us see how this initial concept of the dragon was
reinforced and crystallized by the facts of natural history. To
consider first of all its zoological class, we find that despite
many individual variations there is no doubt that dragons fit
most satisfactorily into the Reptilia. Scales are an essential part

of their equipment, and although some mammals such as the armadillo and the pangolin have a scaly appearance the many other reptilian qualities of dragons make their classification quite certain. Of the three surviving orders of reptiles the snakes and lizards seem to have exercised the most direct and lasting influence. Here are creatures essentially associated with the earth, dwellers in holes who, our ancestors thought, must surely have some direct communication with the underworld. Honours are equally divided between the small poisonous snakes and the large constrictors such as pythons and boas. The latter contributed the conception of size – a large python often measures 30 feet – while the former's venom played a part in the reputed ability of dragons to breathe fire.

Medieval natural histories and bestiaries make frequent allusions to the great length of dragons and their ability to wind themselves round their prey and strangle it to death. Even as late as the seventeenth century we find Edward Topsell recounting in his *Historie of Serpents* (1608) how dragons are actually capable of killing elephants in this way. 'They get and hide themselves in trees', he says, 'covering their head and letting the other part hang downe like a rope. In those trees they watch untill the Elephant comes to eate and croppe of the branches; then suddainly, before he be aware, they leape into his face and digge out his eyes. Then doe they claspe themselves about his necke, and with their tayles or hinder parts, beate and vexe the Elephant, untill they have made him breathlesse, for they strangle him with theyr foreparts, as they beat him with the hinder. . . . And this is the disposition of the Dragon, that he never setteth upon the Elephant but with the advantage of the place, and namely from some high tree or Rock.'

This is simply a highly coloured but quite recognizable account of the way a large python would deal with its prey. Pythons, of course, do not normally come into conflict with elephants, but are quite able to kill gazelles and medium sized antelopes by constriction. Their habit of lying in wait in trees above game trails is quite accurately suggested in Topsell's account.

On the subject of whether or not dragons are venomous Topsell is less explicit. But he does describe how the dragons of Phrygia, when they are hungry, can draw down birds into their throats by the force of their breath. This, he says, according to some, 'is but a voluntary lapse of the fowles, to be drawne by the breath of the dragon, as by a thing they love'; but his own view is that some 'vaporous and venemous breath is sent up from the dragon to them, that poysoneth and infecteth the ayre about them, whereby their senses are taken from them, and they astonished fall downe into his mouth.' This ability of the dragon to breathe venom, or 'fire', is an almost universal feature of the legend and seems to be derived from the poisonous nature of many common species of snakes.

Second to the snakes in the composition of the dragon myth we must give pride of place to the lizards. The majority of dragons are traditionally represented with legs – sometimes two and sometimes four. The ordinary four-legged variety presents no difficulty. It is simply derived from the many common species of lizards distributed all over the world, whose proportions and habits have been exaggerated by travellers' tales and superstitious imaginings. There is in fact an actual living species of lizard, *Varanus komodoensis*, which measures between 10 and 12 feet long and is popularly known as the Komodo dragon. This creature, which comes from the island of Komodo between Flores and Sumbawa in the East Indies, was not officially 'discovered' until 1912. But there is every likelihood that it was sighted by earlier travellers who received vastly inflated impressions of its size from the natives and easily transformed it into the prototype of the legendary dragon.

With the two-legged dragon identification is not quite so straightforward, especially in the various species which were traditionally equipped with wings. These were frequently depicted in the natural histories of the Renaissance and after, the majority resembling that shown in the drawing on the opposite page which is taken from *The History of Serpents and Dragons* (1640) by Ulisse Aldrovandi. The only existing genus of two-legged lizards is *Chirotes*, whose members lead an entirely subterranean life and have no appendages that even the most vivid imagination could mistake for wings. We must therefore look elsewhere for the inspiration of Aldrovandi's dragon and the many others of its kind. And here, as with the sea monk, the most convincing evidence to my mind is that provided by the artificially manufactured Jenny Hanivers described in the last chapter.

A number of peculiar objects which were probably Jenny Haniver dragons were seen in Paris by Hieronimus Cardanus, the great Italian mathematician and physician of Pavia, as

A two-legged winged dragon. From Aldrovandi's *Serpentum et Draconum Historiae* (1640)

long ago as the sixteenth century. He described them as 'two-footed creatures with very small wings, which one could scarcely deem capable of flight, with a small head . . . like a serpent, of a bright colour, and without any feather or hair'. The size of these odd little animals was about that of a small rabbit and they were definitely regarded at the time as dragon babies.

Several theories have been proposed to explain what these creatures actually were. If, as seems likely, they were the originals of the Aldrovandi drawing above and of several variants of it in the works of Petrus Bellonius and others, we can probably assume that they were dried lizards with one pair of legs amputated and bats' wings cunningly grafted on to their sides. The suggestion has also been made that they were mutilated specimens of the little flying lizard *Draco volans* of the Malay Peninsula and the East Indies. This species and its allies are distinguished by having much elongated posterior ribs which support a broad wing-like membrane. The membrane can be extended at will like a fan and enables its owner to glide for short distances through the tree tops.

Another Paris dragon of somewhat similar type was described

by Julius Caesar Scaliger, the sixteenth century commentator on the works of Aristotle and Theophrastus. This conformed even more obviously to the typical Jenny Haniver pattern and may be the inspiration of another particularly sinister dragon illustration in Aldrovandi. Scaliger wrote of this

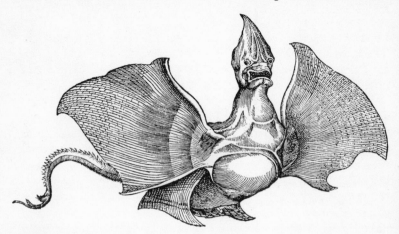

A Jenny Haniver dragon. From Aldrovandi's *Serpentum et Draconum Historiae* (1640)

creature: 'Its head is serrated, and its crest comes to a peak. . . . It has a flexible tail, two feet in length, and bristling with prickles. The skin is like that of a skate.' Here we are surely in the presence of one of those 'improved' skates or rays which, in a different guise, had already contributed valuable detail to the legend of the sea monk.

Finally, before we leave the wicked and sinister dragon of the west and turn to its less formidable eastern counterpart, one further problem remains to be solved. Even the largest python could hardly account for the immense size to which many western dragons were reputed to attain. To explain this we must, I feel, fall back on the evidence derived from the science of palaeontology and particularly from our knowledge of fossil bones found in and around western European caves.

At the time when the dragon legend flourished in western Europe the true nature of fossils was generally unknown. In fact it was not until the nineteenth century that scientists realized that the age of fossil bones often ran into several millions of years. Previously they had been regarded as the remains of individuals who were only recently dead and the great size of some of them was taken as conclusive evidence of the existence of dragons and giants. The extinct animals whose bones were chiefly responsible for this idea were the mammoth (*Elephas primigenius*), the woolly rhinoceros (*Rhinoceros tichorhinus*), and the giant cave bear (*Ursus spelaeus*), all of which were extinct by the end of the Great Ice Age over ten thousand years ago. Today in the Dauphiné of France there is an area still known as *le champ des géants* on account of the numerous remains of ancient elephants that have been found there from time to time.

Whether you favoured the identification of these huge bones with giants or dragons was largely a matter of personal preference. Giants were usually favoured when the bones had any particular likeness to those of human beings, but often, of course, they were entirely dissimilar and then dragons were invoked instead. According to Willy Ley the influence of fossil bones on the dragon legend is well shown in a statue in the market place of the Austrian city of Klagenfurt. This is a representation of a naked giant killing a dragon whose head has obviously been modelled on the skull of a woolly rhinoceros. The connection is proved by the fact that a 'dragon's skull' was in fact found near Klagenfurt in the middle of the sixteenth century, some thirty years before the monument was erected. This skull has been preserved and is now known to be that of *Rhinoceros tichorhinus*.

I hope I have now shown that the western dragon probably arose from a synthesis of several different ideas. First came the primeval fear of darkness and the mysterious and hostile powers of the underworld. To this was added the confirmatory evidence of natural history, derived particularly from experiences with snakes and lizards, told and retold, and becoming more highly coloured with every repetition. Next came the influence of Jenny Hanivers, especially the various adaptations of skates and rays, and the agamid lizards of the genus *Draco*. Finally there was the solid evidence provided by fossil bones.

The dragon built up from these materials was not unnaturally a sinister and fearsome creature associated with all the most hostile features of the natural world. But this was not at all the case with the eastern representative of the genus, whose characteristics we must now describe.

The eastern dragon is perhaps best known from China and it is to the Chinese species that the following remarks refer. It must be borne in mind, however, that other dragon sub-species exist in the east which may differ slightly in habits and even in anatomy. For instance the Japanese dragon, although closely resembling its Chinese relative, is distinguished by having three instead of four claws on each foot.

The authentic Chinese dragon, or Lung, is traditionally supposed to have a camel's head, a deer's horns, a rabbit's eyes, a cow's ears, a snake's neck, a frog's belly, a carp's scales, a hawk's claws and a tiger's palms. Fortunately in its visual respresentations this lavish assemblage of parts has been some-

Chinese dragon. From the Imperial flag of the Manchus

what simplified. The dragon illustrated on this page is taken from the Imperial flag of the Manchus, used up to the establishment of the Republic in 1912, and is typical of the Chinese conception of the creature. Because it is an Imperial dragon it has five toes on each foot, but all other Chinese dragons have only four. Also, like a great number of eastern dragons, it is not depicted with wings.

The Chinese dragon is not, like its western counterpart, a symbol of darkness or evil or in fact of any undesirable quality. Although particularly associated with water it is also an all-pervading element in every myth relating to the powers of nature. There are dragons in the lakes and rivers, in the seas, and even in the raindrops. They are the bringers of abundance and fecundity, the rulers of the storm and the flood, the hidden force behind the waves and the winds. In every natural event the dragons play a part, usually benevolent, sometimes capricious, but only stern and vengeful when their displeasure has been incurred by some foolish or wrongful act of men. They are the leaders of the three hundred and sixty kinds of scaly reptiles and of all other animals, and the pure expression of 'yang', or vital energy, which gives life and light to the Universe.

This mystical, pantheistic quality of the dragons is related in many practical ways to the everyday life of the Chinese, and even the dragons themselves are organized into a social hierachy equivalent to that found in the world of men. The backbone of the dragon world is its government service, divided up into a number of Departments and Ministries with jurisdiction over different aspects of dragon life. Thus there is a Department of Sweet Waters, a General and Special Department of Salt Waters, a Supreme Council of Dragon Ministers and, ruling over all, the Shui Fu or Treasury of Waters, which is ultimately responsible for administering the whole dragon world.

It would be possible to continue indefinitely with such instances of the great charm of the eastern dragon legend, and give further evidence of its supreme importance in Chinese life. But what we are mainly concerned with here is the reason why the legend developed as it did, and why the eastern dragon presents such a strong contrast with the dragon of the west. This, as may be imagined, is a most complicated task, and all one can hope to do in the present context is to make a few tentative suggestions.

It seems probable that the divergence of the legends of western and eastern dragons goes back to the very earliest times. We have already suggested how the western dragon may have become associated with the powers of darkness through the cosmic fear that was a universal emotion in primitive man. This fear, we have said, created the conception of a sun god, a principle of light and life, of whom the dragon was the dark and sinister opponent. Now it seems probable that a very similar process took place in the Far East. There was, however, so far as the dragon was concerned, an extremely important difference. Instead of finding itself allied with the powers of darkness, and therefore appearing as the villain of the piece, it seems to have been cast in exactly the opposite role. The part of the sun god of western mythology is assumed in the east by the dragon, and the more sinister natural forces are largely identified with other symbolical beings such as demons and snakes.

When this fact is realized a great number of seemingly conflicting elements in the two dragon legends fall logically into place. For instance, the common association of the eastern dragon with a ball representing the sun, as on the Manchu flag; the lack of markedly serpentine qualities in the eastern dragon; and the fact that the dragon and the snake are not so widely confused in Chinese mythology as they are in the west. Briefly what seems to have happened is this. From an initial instinct of fear at the strangeness of the Universe both west and east set up symbolical powers to represent on the one hand the forces of light, fecundity, and spiritual strength, and on the other, darkness, evil and other mysterious powers inimical to man. The west cast the sun god in the former role and the dragon in the latter. The east, on the other hand, associated the dragon with the kind of qualities symbolized in the west by the sun god and its role was in consequence reversed.

If this theory is accepted the serpent cannot be regarded as the main component in the natural history of the eastern dragon. Snakes are often worshipped, but they are never associated with benevolence or sublimity, and in any case they already played a distinct role in Chinese mythology. They were everyday objects, respected more for their capacity for doing harm than for any intrinsically supernatural quality. And, as we have already suggested, they were more closely associated with the powers of darkness than with the all pervading majesty of the dragon.

What, then, was the real animal which helped to crystallize the idea of the eastern dragon into its traditional form? This question is not so simply answered as with the dragon of the west, for the Chinese dragon was largely a composite creature derived from several different traditions of animal worship. However, in spite of such varied ingredients as deer, rabbit, cow, hawk, frog, and the rest, the final form of all eastern dragons is strongly reminiscent of one well-known creature – the Chinese alligator of the Lower Yangtze Kiang.

This alligator, scientifically known as *Alligator sinensis*, is the only representative of its genus found in the Old World. Although at present extremely limited in range – it is not found away from certain specific areas in the Yangtze valley – there is evidence to show that in quite recent times it was widely distributed in eastern China. It also seems to be a very ancient species, closely resembling *Alligator thomsoni* of the Miocene Period which came to an end about 15 million years ago.

The association of dragons with water agrees very well with the aquatic habits of the alligator and several Chinese legends confirm the connection between the two creatures. For instance, there is the story of the dragon, or 'spiritual alligator', which transformed itself into a young man, Shên Lang, and married the daughter of the Chief Judge of Yunan. And in Chinese pharmacies sections of dried alligators are sold as magical and pharmaceutical remedies purporting to have been derived from dragons.

With this discussion of the eastern and western legends the natural history of dragons might perhaps be regarded as reasonably well established. There is, however, one other explanation of the dragon that must be mentioned. This is the suggestion, to my mind extremely improbable, that a real dragon-like animal, now of course extinct, once co-existed with early man and was the moving force behind all the legends.

This view was held most strongly at the end of the nineteenth century. Dr N. B. Dennys, an expert on Chinese mythology, declared that there was 'little doubt' that the dragon was the traditional successor of a really once existent creature which was 'the most fearful embodiment of animal ferocity to be found'. Charles Gould, in *Mythical Monsters*, went one better and actually gave a description of the creature and an outline of its habits. 'We may infer', he says, 'that it was a long terrestial lizard, hibernating, and carnivorous, with the power of constricting with its snake-like body and tail; possibly furnished with wing-like expansions of its integument, after the fashion of *Draco volans*, and capable of occasional progress on its hind legs alone, when excited in attack. . . . Probably it preferred sandy, open country to forest land. . . . Although terrestial, it probably, in common with most reptiles, enjoyed frequent bathing, and when not so engaged, or basking in the sun, secluded itself under some overhanging bank or cavern.'

Warming to his theme, Gould concludes his dissertation with the following delightful suggestion:

The idea of its fondness for swallows, and power of attracting them, mentioned in some traditions, may not impossibly have been derived from these birds hawking round and through its open jaws in the pursuit of the flies attracted by the viscid humours of its mouth. We know that at the present day a bird, the trochilus of the ancients, freely enters the open mouth of the crocodile, and rids it of the parasites affecting its teeth and jaws.

Well, nothing is impossible, and it is certainly a fact that the Egyptian plover picks parasites from the jaws of the Nile crocodile. But the idea of swallows performing a similar task for an open-mouthed and grateful dragon is not, I feel, a subject on which a modern naturalist would care to comment.

Finally, there is one other theory based on the possible existence of a real extinct dragon which invokes the concept of racial memory. This was proposed by Dr Edgard Dacqué, a former professor of geology at Munich University, who cast for the role of dragon the giant carnivorous dinosaurs of the Mesozoic Era. But because the last dinosaur became extinct some 60-70 million years before the evolution of the first man, Dacqué had to suggest that the 'memory' of these creatures was transmitted to men by such lemur-like ancestors of his who had happened to be there at the time.

Certainly it must be agreed that the carnivorous dinosaurs were sufficiently awe-inspiring to be compared with the most fearsome of legendary dragons. This will become doubly apparent in the second part of this book when we shall look at some of the dinosaurs in more detail. But that racial memory actually occurs is the most doubtful of propositions. In any investigation it is surely the most flagrant form of cheating to invent a process that will explain the facts and then assume its existence for that reason. And, as we have already seen, the explanation of the dragon legend requires no such arbitary assumptions for it can be fully accounted for in terms of existing facts. To my mind the dragon, like the mermaid and a dozen other mythological beings, was originally a symbol created by men in answer to some inner need. The form of this symbol was first suggested, and then modified in different areas, by the observable facts of natural history. A combination of these psychological and physical influences is surely sufficient to give the dragon an awe-inspiring reality without our needing to embark on a futile search for its fossil bones.

CHAPTER FIVE

Fabulous Ornithology

Many strange birds are on the air abroad,
Nor are all of one flights of one force,
But each after his kind dissimilar.

GUIDO GUINICELLI:
Of Moderation and Tolerance

I have to enquire, with the help of God, what real truth there is
in the Phoenix.

GEORGE CASPARD KIRCHMAYER:
Hexas disputationum Zoologicanum (1661)

And. . . . behold the sun became concealed from us, and the
day grew dark, and there came over us a cloud by which the sky
was obscured. So we raised our heads to see what had intervened
between us and the sun, and saw that the wings of the rukh were
what veiled from us the sun's light, so that the sky was darkened.

THE ARABIAN NIGHTS:
The Fifth Voyage of Es-Sindibad of the Sea

IN considering the ornithology of fabulous birds we find ourselves in one of the most interesting and poetical territories of
the world of myth. Birds belong to the air – an ethereal
region of purity and light – and the symbolism associated with
them has none of the sinister qualities belonging to serpents
and the more formidable species of dragons. They are symbols
of hope and regeneration, representing the highest aspirations of
mankind.

Even today birds play a large part in the totemism of primitive tribes. The American Indians especially have adapted bird
symbolism as an important factor in their daily life, and no
boy scout would need to be reminded how owls, eagles, peewits
and other birds have survived even into our own society as the
distinguishing symbols of their patrols, or 'tribes'. Moreover
the identification of birds and bird symbols with everyday life
goes back to the remotest antiquity. For example, in the depths
of the famous Lascaux caves in the Dordogne region of south-

western France there is a drawing of an enigmatical bird-man who must certainly have been associated with some form of primitive ritual. The age of these cave paintings is at the latest Upper Palaeolithic and some authorities believe they date from over 30,000 years ago.

But in spite of the bird-man of Lascaux, the oldest and most famous bird legends appear in the main to have originated in

The Gryphon. An illustration by John Tenniel from *Alice in Wonderland*

the east. As the traditional stories moved westward they became adulterated with alien elements, and the birds themselves began to lose their kindly and benevolent natures. Thus the gryphon, the most famous bird-like creature of western mythology, although undoubtedly associated in the Middle Ages with the sun, was not a typical legendary bird, but a kind of mongrel, half bird half mammal. Readers of Lewis Carroll will doubtless recall Alice's first encounter with a gryphon when being taken by the Queen to meet the Mock Turtle: 'They very soon came upon a Gryphon, lying asleep in the sun. (If you don't know what a Gryphon is, look at the picture) . . . Alice did not quite like the look of the creature. . . .' The Tenniel illustration gives an excellent idea of the traditional conception of a gryphon – a creature with the upper half of a

79

bird and the lower half of a lion. This, it has been suggested, was the result of the Common heraldic practice of 'dimidiation' – that is, the combination of the coats of arms of husband and wife by joining half of the one to the opposite half of the other. Despite Alice's fears the gryphon turned out to be a harmless if somewhat vapid and inconsequential creature, but this was not typical of other western members of the genus. The western gryphon was normally regarded as a highly predacious animal whose fierce and implacable nature was most aptly symbolized by its wicked curved beak and powerful claws. (There was incidentally at one time a brisk trade in these 'gryphon's claws' which travellers brought back from Africa and the east and were identified by a later and less credulous generation as the horns of antelope.)

The gryphon, then, is not typical of the majestic bird gods of earlier times, and has been mentioned here only because of its fame as an heraldic animal in western Europe. Nor can it be said to have a proper natural history, for its ancestry is too mixed and uncertain, and it is too remote from its natural origins. For the ancestral legendary birds, and for the real creatures associated with them, we have to leave Europe altogether and travel eastwards towards the land of the rising sun.

The most ancient and magnificent of all the birds in mythology is probably Garuda, the sacred bird of India, who is especially associated with Vishnu, the second person in the triad of Hindu deities. Vishnu is a personification of the preserving power, and Garuda the emblem of strength and swiftness who bears him on his various benevolent missions on behalf of men. Through the ages images of Garuda have been set up in the temples of Vishnu and worshipped with those of the god. It even seems probable that Garuda is older than Vishnu – a direct survival of nature worship – and became associated with and partly subservient to the god only as a result of the admixture of anthropomorphic elements in primitive religion. This would also account for the partially human characters that appear in some of the images of the bird.

Now what of Garuda's natural history? This, as with so many of the other animal legends we have been considering, can only be understood by taking both psychological and zoological elements into account. In prehistoric times, when men sought gods in the forces of nature, a bird deity was the obvious choice to symbolize the sky, for birds were the only creatures who naturally belonged to that element. It was also

Garuda, by Anne Marie Jauss after Cambodian sculptures. From Peter Lum's *Fabulous Beasts*. (Reproduced by permission of Messrs Thames & Hudson Ltd.)

natural that the largest and most powerful of birds should first attract the attention of primitive man; and for this reason the ancestral Garuda was probably first identified with one of the great Indian birds of prey.

Eagles and other large predatory birds are well represented in India, particularly in the north, where the magnificent

Pallas's fishing eagle, *Haliaëtus leucoryphus*, is common on the alluvial plains of the Ganges and the Indus. Further north still, along the Himalayas and their tributary ranges, the huge Lämmergeier makes its home. This splendid bird, otherwise known as *Gypaëtus barbatus*, the bearded vulture, has a wing span of over ten feet and can often be observed beating along the mountain sides on the look-out for carrion. It is particularly fond of large bones, which it breaks into manageable pieces by carrying them up to a great height and then dropping them on to the rocky ground below. In the eastern Mediterranean this habit, which is also applied to tortoises, may well have accounted for the death of Aeschylus, who is alleged to have been killed by having a tortoise dropped on his head.

Other well-known birds of northern India extend their range much further south. The most common of all Indian birds of prey is the tawny eagle, *Aquila rapax vindhiana*, which is found everywhere except in Ceylon and along the Malabar coast. Another bird particularly interesting to our present theme is the crested serpent eagle, *Haematornis cheela*, whose three different races cover the whole of the country. This bird feeds almost entirely on snakes and other reptiles and can frequently be seen in the paddy fields, a snake writhing in its talons. It is perhaps significant that Garuda was regarded as the traditional enemy of snakes and his image was embraced by all those suffering from snake-bite in the belief that he alone of the Hindu demi-gods could have power to cure them. In fact one of the alternative names of Garuda is Nag-antaka, the enemy of serpents.

Now it seems probable that all these birds have played a part in Garuda's ancestry, for their size and majestic appearance is admirably suited to a god-like role. Yet surprisingly enough in India today the bird identified with Garuda is none of these, but a very much smaller and comparatively unimpressive bird of prey which is, however, extremely common in wetter districts and along the coast. This bird is the Brahminy kite, *Haliastur indus*, and its connection with the legend has even been recognized by one of the pundits of zoological nomenclature, who has bestowed on it the alternative scientific name of *Haliaëtus garuda*.

Among the Hindus the Brahminy kite is regarded as a sacred animal, and even in the colouring of the bird the pious can recognize the likeness of Garuda. The traditional description of the demi-god tells how he had a white face, red wings and a golden body; the plumage of the Brahminy kite is a golden chestnut red, while the head and the breast as far as the abdomen is white.

Like the sacred cow, the Brahminy kite is never killed. This is partly due to its religious significance, but partly also we may suspect, because of its great value in crowded sea-port towns in removing carrion and refuse. Often on religious holidays

The Brahminy kite, *Haliastur indus*

the pious Hindu can be seen giving offerings of meat to the bird, throwing them into the air where they are deftly caught as black-headed gulls catch bacon rind in the London parks.

One result of the Brahminy kite's privileged position is that it has become exceptionally bold. Towards the end of the war, when I was stationed in Calcutta, a great number of these birds, together with specimens of the pariah kite, *Milvus migrans*, used to circle the R.A.F. transit camp at meal times. One of the favourite, if slightly malicious, amusements of those of us who were old stagers in the city was to watch the adventures of airmen newly arrived from Britain who were as yet unaware of the local hazards. In order to pass from the serving hatches in the cook house to the tables set aside for eating one had to cross a small open air courtyard with a mug of tea and plate of food. Above this courtyard were congregated the Brahminy kites, waiting for the first unsuspecting airman to make the perilous journey without first taking the precaution of covering his plate with his hand. There would then be a harsh cry and a flurry of wings as one of the watchful kites 'stooped' onto the plate and carried off the bacon or fried liver that the airman was about to have for his breakfast. I should perhaps add that no airman who was caught by this kind of surprise attack was allowed to return for a second breakfast and it was therefore seldom that a bird claimed the same victim twice.

The Phoenix. A drawing by Anne Marie Jauss in Peter Lum's *Fabulous Beasts*. (Reproduced by permission of Messrs Thames & Hudson Ltd.)

So much, then, for Garuda, the sacred bird of the east. For the natural history of our second bird we must move westwards to Africa, and more especially to Egypt. Here, at Heliopolis, the City of the Sun, near Cairo, was the focus of that most famous of all legends of fabulous birds – the legend of the phoenix.

The phoenix legend, like that of Garuda, is a very ancient one, and as it is also exceptionally beautiful I hope I may be forgiven if I recount it at some length. According to tradition there could only be one phoenix in the world at a time. It dwelt in paradise, which in the eyes of the ancients was a land of infinite beauty lying beyond the horizon towards the rising sun. There was no sorrow in paradise and no death, and it was a region that no mortal eye could ever see. At intervals of 1,000 years – some versions of the story say 350 or 500 years, or even 1,461, which corresponded with the Sothic cycle of the Egyptian calendar – the phoenix became oppressed by the growing burden of the centuries and knew that at last it had to die. Accordingly, as death was impossible in paradise, it left its wonderful home and took wing for the mortal world. It flew westward over the jungles of Burma and Assam, the hot plains of central India, and the mountains of Afghanistan, until it came at length to the spice groves of Arabia. Here it paused in its journey to load its wings with a sweet-perfumed cargo of laudanum and frankincense and other aromatic plants, and then flew on until it came to the coast that is named after it, the coast of Phoenicia, in Syria, running northwards from Mount Carmel.

Along this coast the palm trees grew in profusion, and the phoenix took the aromatic plants it had gathered and began to build itself a nest high up among the topmost branches of the tallest tree. At last, as night fell, its labours were completed, and it settled down to await the dawn that it knew would herald its death.

The hours of darkness passed slowly, but at last the sky lightened and the sun soared upwards over the horizon. As it did so the phoenix turned to the east and sang a song of such surpassing beauty that even the sun god himself paused for a second in his chariot to listen. And in that moment the whole Universe, the rolling Earth and the wheeling stars, stood still with the sun god and listened to the sweetness of the phoenix's song. Then as suddenly as he had paused the sun god whipped up his horses again. Sparks flew from their hooves and from the vast corona of fire that encircled his head. Some of these sparks fell on the nest of the phoenix, and catching the sweet smelling herbs, turned it to a blazing aromatic funeral pyre. And thus in song and perfume and fire the phoenix ended its thousand years of life.

But although the phoenix was dead the story was not yet quite ended. As the ashes of the nest cooled, a little worm could be seen stirring in the remains of the phoenix's body. Within three days the worm had grown and changed into a new phoenix. As soon as it was strong enough this bird collected the ashes of its predecessor into a ball of myrrh and flew with them to Heliopolis and laid them reverently on the altar of the sun god. Then it winged its way eastward to spend the next thousand years in paradise, when its own turn would come to return to the mortal world and die. On this part of its journey, however, the new phoenix did not fly alone. It was accompanied by a vast concourse of birds of every size and description which flew together in the greatest amity, even such natural enemies as the great hawks and eagles and the little birds of the under-growth. Only when they reached the borders of paradise, which the phoenix alone could enter, did this retinue turn back to the world of strife and sorrow.

To modern students of mythology the symbolism of this beautiful legend of the phoenix is not difficult to understand. The phoenix is the bird of the sun, and at the same time re-presents the sun itself. Like the sun it comes from the east, bearing on its wings the pungent odours of Arabia. And as the bird of the sun, it is immolated in the splendour of the tropical sunrise when the first rays touch the leaves of the tallest palm tree and turn them to fire.

But the natural history of the phoenix is more difficult. More obviously than many legendary creatures its story belongs to the imagination, and its association with a real bird is of secondary importance. Yet, as always in legend, this is not the whole truth. Behind the poetry of the symbolism some actual living creature must have played a part.

To arrive at the identification of the phoenix with a real bird it is necessary first of all to visualize it. The earliest literary description of it is in the second book of the *Histories* of Hero-dotus, written in the fifth century B.C. Herodotus writes: 'There is also a sacred bird called the phoenix, which I have never seen except in a picture. . . . If he is like the picture, he is of the following size and description: the plumage of his wings is partly golden coloured, and partly red: in outline and size he is very like an eagle.'

Well, this is possibly a correct description, but it is perhaps significant that it could apply equally well to Garuda and to other fabulous birds of the time such as the Persian senmurv and simurg, which also resembled large birds of prey. It seems at least possible that Herodotus, who admitted that he had not seen the phoenix, had been misled into confusing two separate legends. This point of view is confirmed 500 years later by Pliny in his *Natural History*, who gives a somewhat different description of the phoenix. 'By report', he says (again using Philemon Holland's translation), 'he is as big as an Æagle; for colour, as yellow and bright as gold; (namely, all about the neck;) the rest of the bodie a deepe red purple: the taile azure blew, intermingled with feathers among, of rose cornation colour: and the head bravely adorned with a crest and pennache finely wrought; having a tuft and plume thereupon, right faire and goodly to be seene.' That this description does indeed apply to the phoenix and not to some other bird he confirmed by the following delightful reference to the legend, quoted from one Manilius, a Roman senator who had a high reputation for learning: 'Of his bones and marrow there breedeth at first as it were a little worme: which afterwards proveth to bee a pretie bird: And the first thing that this yong new Phoenix doth, is to performe the obsequies of the former Phoenix late deceased.'

The tuft and plume, and the purple colour of the body mentioned by Pliny, give any ornithologist a very strong hint as to what bird the phoenix may actually have been. There is in Egypt even now a large purplish bird with a well defined crest which is strongly reminiscent of Pliny's description and whose habits are consistent with several aspects of the phoenix legend. This is the purple heron, *Ardea purpurea*, which has also occasionally been recorded as a visitor to this country.

Now the purple heron is very similar to our own grey heron, *Ardea cinerea*, which is also found in Egypt. And as every countryman knows, the grey heron habitually builds its nest in the top of the tallest trees. It is surely not too far fetched to see the association between the phoenix, which built its nest in the tallest palm tree and was also described by Pliny as purple and crested, with these two large herons of the genus *Ardea*. This suggestion is also supported by ancient Egyptian pictures of the phoenix, which show it to have had a very heron-like shape. But if doubt remains there is still further corroboration. In Egypt the local name for the purple heron is 'benu', a word which in the Egyptian tongue means 'palm tree'. And in translations of the famous *Book of the Dead* and other Egyptian texts, we can read how the benu was one of the symbols of the worship of the sun god at Heliopolis. Finally, what is perhaps the most conclusive evidence of all comes from ancient Greek, the

The purple heron, *Ardea purpurea*

language through which the legend of the phoenix was first transmitted to the western world. The Greek word for palm tree, transliterated into the letters of our own alphabet, is none other than 'phoenix'.

It would be fascinating to pursue this question of the identification of legendary birds into other ages and different parts of the world. For instance, there is much research still to be done on the origin of the Chinese phoenix, or *Fung Hwang*, which is a quite different bird from the Egyptian variety and seems to be associated with one of the numerous species of pheasants. But in the limits of a single chapter I must restrict myself to only one other example which will provide a kind of connecting link with the material to be dealt with in the second part of this book. This is the giant legendary bird of the south, known as the rukh or roc, which has been famous in legend for over a thousand years.

The earliest mention of the rukh occurs in the *Thousand and One Nights*, the famous collection of Arab tales which was

The Rukh. From a Persian drawing reproduced in Lane's *Arabian Nights*

already old when William of Normandy sailed for England. Here, in the stories of the Third Royal Mendicant, of Hasan of El-Basrah, and above all in the account of the Second and Fifth Voyages of Es-Sindibad of the Sea, we read of an enormous white bird which made its home on a 'beautiful island, abounding with trees bearing ripe fruits, where flowers diffused their fragrance, with birds warbling, and pure rivers'. So huge was it that the length of the wing of the young rukh at the time of its coming out of the egg was a thousand fathoms, and the quills of its wing feathers held as much water as a goat's skin.

Es-Sindibad, – or Sinbad the Sailor, to give him his more

usual name – mistook the egg itself for a huge white dome of great height and large circumference. 'I drew near to it', he says, 'and walked round it, but perceived no door to it; and I found that I had not strength nor activity to climb it, on account of its exceeding smoothness. I made a mark at the place where I stood, and went round the dome measuring its circumference, and, lo, it was fifty full paces; and I meditated upon some means of gaining an entrance into it.'

While thus engaged, Sinbad noticed that the sun was hidden and the sky had become darkened. He continues: 'I therefore imagined that a cloud had come over it; but this was in the season of summer; so I wondered. And I raised my head, and, contemplating that object attentively, I saw that it was a bird, of enormous size, bulky body, and wide wings, flying in the air; and this it was that concealed the body of the sun, and veiled it from view upon the island. At this my wonder increased, and I remembered a story which travellers and voyagers had told me long before, that there is in certain of the islands, a bird of enormous size, called the rukh, that feedeth its young ones with elephants. I was convinced, therefore, that the dome which I had seen was one of the eggs of the rukh. I wondered at the works of God (whose name be exalted!); and while I was in this state, lo, that bird alighted upon the dome, and brooded over it with its wings, stretching out its legs behind upon the ground; and it slept over it.'

At a later stage in Sinbad's adventures some merchants broke the egg and in revenge the rukh and its mate dropped huge pieces of stone on Sinbad's ship and sank it. The rukh is also mentioned by Marco Polo, who says that 'its wings covered an extent of 30 paces, and its quills were 12 paces long, and thick in proportion.' He comments on the great strength of the bird which enables it to kill elephants by lifting them high in the air and dropping them so that they are smashed to pieces. Finally he tells us how the Great Khan sent an envoy to enquire into the truth of these stories, and that this emissary brought back a feather measuring 90 spans in length and was handsomely rewarded with 'great presents'.

From the various descriptions of the beautiful island where the rukh was reputed to dwell it can be safely identified as Madagascar. In fact Marco Polo actually mentions it by name.

Have we, then, any evidence of a real bird inhabiting this great island which might have inspired the legend of the rukh?

Among modern species the answer is definitely 'no'. The only local eagle is the Madagascar sea eagle, *Concuma vociferoïdes*, which measures little over two feet in length, while among the large ground birds such as the ostrich, cassowary and emu, there is no living representative. But when we turn our attention to extinct birds we find ourselves at once in a more profitable field.

In the year 1661 there appeared in Paris a complete *History of Madagascar* by one Étienne de Flacourt, a French governor of the island. In this work de Flacourt spoke of a giant bird which used to inhabit the southern part of Madagascar and lay gigantic eggs. From the seventeenth to nineteenth centuries the position of the French in Madagascar was extremely insecure, and de Flacourt's interesting observation does not seem to have attracted much attention. But in the year 1832 a traveller in Madagascar named Sganzin sent a picture of a gigantic egg to the French naturalist Jules Verreaux in Cape Town. The picture has been lost, but the letter accompanying it is still extant and describes how the natives of Madagascar used these huge eggs as vessels for holding liquids.

During the next few years further reports concerning the eggs came in, notably one from John Joliffe, a ship's doctor on board the British vessel *Geyser*. Joliffe told Hugh Strickland, the British expert on the dodo and other extinct birds, how several of the eggs had been seen in use on the north coast of Madagascar; attempts had been made to purchase one, but unfortunately without success. Finally, in 1850, a French sea captain named Abadie got hold of some bones and egg fragments which he sent to the Academy of Sciences in Paris. They were described to the Academy the following year by the French zoologist Isidore Geoffroy-Saint-Hilaire, who referred them to a new kind of gigantic extinct bird which he named *Aepyornis maximus*.

There seems little doubt that these eggs, and the birds that laid them, inspired the legend of the rukh. Although not as large as the 'dome' discovered by Sinbad the Sailor, they are nevertheless the largest known to science. One example measures no less than $12\frac{1}{4}$ by $9\frac{3}{8}$ inches, which gives it a capacity of 2.35 gallons. This is equivalent to 6 ostrich eggs, or 148 eggs of the common domestic fowl.

Now what were the birds like that laid these fantastic eggs, and when did they die out? From the legend as told in the *Arabian Nights* and *Marco Polo's Travels* we might assume that they had the general shape of an eagle, but this has not proved

Aepyornis maximus, the giant extinct bird that probably inspired the legend of the rukh

to be the case. The eagle element in the legend seems to have originated in a confusion with Garuda and other bird gods such as the anka and simurg of the Middle East. The hundreds of fossil bones that have now been found in Madagascar show that *Aepyornis* was in fact a huge flightless bird like a giant ostrich. Its nearest known relation is the extinct *Dinornis*, or moa, of New Zealand.

Several species of *Aepyornis* are now recognized, the largest still being *Aepyornis maximus*. The mounted skeleton of this bird in the Natural History Museum in Paris has a height of just under ten feet. Alfred Wallace believed that the bird may have existed alive in Madagascar until about 250 years ago, but he did not quote any evidence in support of his opinion. Other rumours say that it survived until the beginning of the nineteenth century. Although this last view can safely be discounted, there is no reason to doubt that *Aepyornis* was very much alive during the first millennium of the Christian Era.

Judging from the areas in which the eggs were found *in situ*, these giant birds were most at home in dry desert country. When Alfred Grandidier visited Madagascar in 1866 on board the trading ship *Indefatigable* he found numerous egg fragments in the region of Cape St. Mary, the southernmost tip of the island. Here, beyond a narrow sandy beach, there are a series of sand-dunes rising to a height of about 450 feet. Two separate tiers can be discerned which at a distance resemble man-made fortifications. Between them is a flat plateau which, like the dunes, is dotted with clumps of prickly bushes almost indistinguishable in their drab foliage from the soil on which they grow. This inhospitable country, almost waterless and open to the violence of every southern gale, was once, it seems, the home of *Aepyornis*.

The connection of *Aepyornis* with the rukh will by now be readily apparent, but before concluding I would like just to mention two subsidiary aspects of the legend which strike me as being particularly interesting. In the first place the story of a pair of rukhs dropping great stones on Sinbad's ship has obviously originated in a real experience of meteorites. It is quite natural that a primitive people would associate these mysterious missiles from outer space with a gigantic bird god taking vengeance on men. In the second place there is a very simple explanation of the gigantic feather which the Great Khan's emissary is said to have brought back to his master from Madagascar. This was almost certainly a frond of the well-known Madagascan palm tree known as *Sagus ruffia*, the rofia palm, whose trunk sometimes measures 50 feet or more in height. It divides at the top into seven or eight long fronds whose central shaft may be as thick at the base as a man's thigh, while the whole frond would be strongly reminiscent of the feather of a giant bird. Thus not only in the rukh itself, but in several comparatively minor details of its appearance and behaviour, we can see the perennial influence of natural science on the formation of legends.

PART TWO

Stone Testament

CHAPTER SIX

The Book of Earth History

Thus saith the Lord God unto these bones: Behold, I will cause breath to enter into you, and ye shall live: and I will lay sinews upon you, and will bring up flesh upon you, and cover you with skin ... and ye shall live; and ye shall know that I am the Lord.

EZEKIEL: *Ch. 37. vv.* 5 & 6

There rolls the deep where grew the tree.
O earth, what changes hast thou seen!
There where the long street roars, hath been
The stillness of the central sea.

The hills are shadows, and they flow
From form to form, and nothing stands;
They melt like mist, the solid lands,
Like clouds they shape themselves and go.

TENNYSON: *In Memoriam*

ONE of the most intriguing aspects of some of the animal legends we have just described is the way their growth was influenced by fossil bones. Until quite recently men have always been puzzled by fossils, and it was natural that in default of a more satisfactory explanation they should regard them as evidence of the real existence of giants and dragons. In one sense, also, these superstitious theories were not so very far wide of the mark. Many fossils bear witness to the former existence of creatures which were much more horrific than the most formidable dragon conjured up by the human imagination.

In the next few chapters we shall consider some of the facts now known about these real giants and dragons of the past. We shall tell how their remains were discovered and how the evidence concerning their natural history came to be interpreted. First, however, to make the story more comprehensible, we must be a little more explicit about the actual nature of fossils and give the background of the two comparatively young sciences of geology and palaeontology which have revealed their true significance.

Fossils, broadly speaking, are the remains of prehistoric animals and plants embedded in the rocks of the Earth's crust. Footprints, the marks of raindrops, and cracks in sun-baked mud can also be preserved in a fossil state, as can the impressions of leaves and natural casts of the shapes of animals which may persist long after the actual tissues have mouldered away. The way that animals came to be buried deep in the surface of the Earth was for centuries a great problem to men. But now we know that the great majority of these remains were preserved through being covered, shortly after the death of the animal, by water-borne sediments on the beds of rivers or the floors of seas. Alternatively the animal sometimes became mired in peat bogs or deposits of natural asphalt, or died in hot deserts and was covered by wind-blown sand. The deposits in which its remains were entombed then gradually hardened into solid rock which subsided or became deformed or upraised according to the stresses and strains operating in the Earth's crust during the succeeding millennia. Finally the remains, now changed by mineral action into fossils, were occasionally re-exposed to view, either by natural erosive forces such as wind and rain and ice, or by man-made incisions in the Earth's crust such as mines and quarries.

Of course the natural forces responsible for the original entombment and the eventual re-exposure of the fossils took an immense period of time to operate, and it is now known that the first sedimentary rocks in the history of the earth were laid down well over a thousand million years ago. This knowledge resulted from the discoveries of the British geologists James Hutton and Sir Charles Lyell, working respectively in the eighteenth and nineteenth centuries, and is therefore of comparatively recent date. Previously the Christian world had believed that the Earth had existed for rather less than six thousand years – an opinion based on the mathematical fantasies of the seventeenth century Irish archbishop James Usher, who being nothing if not an exact man, had worked out from the Old Testament that God had begun the creation at 8 p.m. on Saturday October 22nd 4004 B.C. This, as may be imagined, was quite an inadequate allowance of time for the production of fossils, and it confirmed the popular view that when remains were found they must belong to giants or dragon-like animals whose relatives were either still alive or at least only recently extinct.

Forgetting for a moment the knowledge that has been given to us by modern geology and palaeontology, let us now go back for a moment to the days of early human history and see what men thought when they first became preoccupied with the problem of fossils. The great Greek historian Herodotus, who was born at Halicarnassus about 484 B.C., is usually credited with being the first to make observations on the subject. He was, however, forestalled by two earlier writers, the philosopher Xenophanes of Colophon, and the Lydian chronicler Xanthus of Sardis. The works of Xenophanes, whose long life extended over nearly the whole of the sixth century B.C., have nearly all been lost, but quotations by later classical writers show that he had observed the remains of fossilized marine molluscs on mountains far inland and had deduced, quite rightly, that these areas had once been covered by the sea. He had also seen fossil imprints of laurel leaves in rocks on the island of Paros, which enables us to regard him as the first palaeobotanist, as students of fossil plants are technically called. Xanthus, who lived about a generation before Herodotus, had examined fossil shells in the interior of Asia Minor, and also drawn a completely accurate conclusion concerning them – namely that they had once been alive where they now were, and that the boundaries of sea and land must therefore be undergoing constant change.

The contribution of Herodotus himself was to record the presence of shells on high ground in Egypt many miles from the sea. In the second book of the *Histories* he tells how he deduced from this fact, as well as from the configuration of the Nile delta and the quality of the soil, that the sea had once transgressed far inland over this part of Africa. The correctness of his view was confirmed over two thousand years later when a scientific examination of the shells disclosed that they belonged to marine bivalves.

The great Aristotle of Stagira, who lived from 384 to 322 B.C., commented in a general way on fossils, and his work was developed by his pupil Theophrastus in a book which has now unfortunately been lost. But neither Aristotle nor Theophrastus seems to have had as clear a vision as their predecessors of the subject. They regarded fossils as belonging to a quite separate and inferior order of nature, and believed that they had been spontaneously generated in the rocks by a mysterious plastic force.

With the decline of Greece the first accurate glimpses of the nature of fossils were completely lost sight of, and in Roman times we already see the beginnings of the superstitious views concerning them that were later to characterize the Middle Ages. For example, the Emperor Augustus, who had anticipated modern artists and film stars by discovering the charms of Capri, was reputed by Suetonius to have decorated his villa there with enormous fossil bones. These were generally regarded at the time as the remains of a giant race.

After the long night of the Dark Ages the fossil question once more became a subject of learned argument. The scholars of that time were mainly clerics and it was therefore not surprising that someone soon hit on the brilliant idea that fossils must be the remains of animals that had been drowned in the Biblical Flood. This point of view still found favour as late as the eighteenth century and even after, and was particularly encouraged by a German physician named Johann Scheuchzer who in 1726 triumphantly produced the supposed fossil skeleton of a drowned human being. This he identified as 'one of those infamous men whose sins brought upon the world the dire misfortune of the deluge'. It was perhaps fortunate that Scheuchzer was already dead when a few years later the skeleton was found to belong to an extinct species of giant salamander.

Despite this setback the Flood theory showed remarkable resilience. It even withstood the early onslaughts of scientific geology which showed conclusively that fossils were found in strata that had at one time been buried several miles deep in the Earth. The answer of the Diluvialists, as they were called, to this revelation, was that the Flood must have reduced the Earth's surface to a pasty mass in which the drowned animals sank to varying depths; when the waters retreated this paste hardened into solid rock with the bones distributed throughout the whole crust. Sometimes, they added, the gases exhaling from the putrefying carcases formed bubbles in the solidifying paste; this accounted for the origin of caves, and of the bones often found in them.

But the Diluvialists did not have a monopoly of the picturesque.

Dead giants were always regarded as the most likely source of the larger fossils, and several entertaining anecdotes are associated with this time-honoured theory. For instance in the early seventeenth century a lively controversy was carried on concerning the authenticity of an alleged giant's grave that had been discovered in the Dauphiné region of France. The saga began with the publication in 1613 of a pamphlet with the somewhat pretentious name of *Gygantosteologie*, by one Nicolas Habicot, a professor of surgery in the University of Paris. Habicot claimed that on Friday January 11th 1613, near the château of Chaumont in the Dauphiné, some quarrymen had come across a huge stone coffin measuring 30 feet long by 12 feet wide by 8 feet deep. The coffin was buried at a depth of 18 feet below ground and contained a gigantic human skeleton no less than 25½ feet in length. The remains had been examined by a surgeon called Pierre Mazuyer, who had reported that the giant to whom they belonged had measured 10 feet across the shoulders, had eye sockets as big as dinner plates and a skull 5 feet long and 10 feet in circumference. Most remarkable of all, the grey stone slab that covered the coffin had been inscribed 'Teutobochus Rex' – the name of a barbarian leader who had been overcome by the Roman general Caius Marius in the second century B.C.

A thin enough story, one would have thought, but it seems at first to have been remarkably successful. The discoverers of the 'giant' paraded some of the bones through the larger cities of France, arriving finally in a blaze of glory at Paris. The complete skeleton, they said, was unfortunately not available, for by an unhappy chance 'most of the bones, after exposure to the air from 8 a.m. to 6 p.m., had crumbled to powder'. Yet the parts that remained, consisting of two vertebrae, two fragments of the lower jaw, part of a shoulder blade, and some limb bones from the left side of the body, were apparently sufficiently impressive to net a handsome profit from credulous sightseers *en route*.

At last, however, even in those superstitious days, someone scented a fraud. The well-known anatomist and surgeon Jean Riolan brought out a pamphlet entitled *Gigantologie* denouncing Mazuyer's giant as an impostor. But even he was not prepared to say more than that the size of the skeleton had been considerably exaggerated. Finally the matter reached the French

Academy of Sciences. In a battle royal between the rival factions the bones were variously regarded as the genuine remains of some human or animal giant, or as mineral freaks of nature. It was not until over two centuries after the original discovery that King Teutobochus became correctly docketed in the annals of palaeontology as an early member of the elephant family with the name *Dinotherium* or 'huge beast'.

The more pious among the advocates of the giant theory believed that all large bones belonged to the patriarchs of the Old Testament. These were regarded as having been exceptionally tall men because they were known to have lived to a great age. One early eighteenth century writer actually worked out the height of the patriarchs on this assumption. Thus Adam was asserted to have been 123 feet 9 inches tall, Noah just over 100 feet, and so on, the height decreasing proportionately as more modern times were approached.

Alongside the giant hypothesis several less hackneyed themes were being developed. Thus some maintained that fossils resulted from exhalations from the Earth or seeds that fell from the stars; others that the rocks themselves produced the fossils, which explained why different kinds of fossils were found in different strata. One particularly charming view was that fossils were the original moulds used by the Creator in fashioning the different kinds of animals and plants.

Despite the many strange theories put forward to explain what fossils were, their physical appearance was well known from early Renaissance times and they were illustrated in many books of natural history. Thus Conrad Gesner's *Historiae Animalium* (1565) includes a picture of a fossil belemnite, while a hundred years later there are some magnificent illustrations of fossil fish in the *Mundus Subterraneus* of Athanasius Kircher. But the most intriguing book to include illustrations of fossils is that known as *Lithographica Würceburgensis*, published in 1726 by a professor in the University of Würzburg called Johannes Beringer. Alongside a number of genuine fossils from Bavaria, which we now know to date from the geological period called the Triassic, the reader is astonished to see representations of the sun and moon and other celestial bodies, and even of letters from the Hebrew alphabet. And thereby hangs a half comic, half tragic story.

Apparently it was Beringer's practice to take his students on trips into the countryside round Würzburg in search of fossils. Often the results of these expeditions were extremely successful, as is proved by the real fossils shown in the book. But after a time the novelty of fossil hunting began to pall on the high-spirited students and they decided to enliven the proceedings by manufacturing fossils of their own and placing them in situations where the professor was certain to find them. The unsuspecting Beringer made a large collection of these curiosities, whose authenticity he did not doubt for a moment, and then sat down to write his monograph. Shortly after it was published, however, one of the students overstepped the mark by planting a fossil inscribed with Beringer's own name. The poor old man immediately realized that he had been the victim of a cruel but entirely successful hoax. He spent his entire savings in an attempt to buy up all the copies of his book, but his reputation had gone beyond hope of recall. The book itself was reprinted as a scientific curiosity in 1677, and the *Lügensteine*, or 'false fossils', were distributed among German museums and university collections where many of them can still be seen.

In addition to contributions from lesser lights, the early history of fossils in Europe was distinguished by pronounce-ments from two of the world's universal geniuses, Leonardo da Vinci and Voltaire. Leonardo was the first authority since classi-cal times to recognize fossils for what they were. In the late fifteenth century the building of canals in Italy had revealed the presence of large numbers of fossil sea shells, which caused Leonardo to make the accurate observation that these areas must formerly have been covered by the sea. Voltaire's con-tribution was less fortunate. While living at Ferney in Switzer-land in the latter part of his life he noticed deposits of sea shells on the slopes of the Alps. But the true explanation of this phenomenon escaped him, and his statement that they were probably the remains left by pilgrims picnicking off shell fish on their way to Rome must be regarded as one of his less memorable intellectual flights.

But we must now turn from these lighter aspects of the story to the way that the study of fossils was finally put on a scientific footing. Apart from the early Greeks and Leonardo da Vinci, two investigators are especially important before the end of the eighteenth century. A French pottery maker named Bernard Palissy, who died in 1589, had not only recognized the true nature of fossils but actually identified the species of several of them according to correct scientific principles. In the following century Nicolaus Steno, a Danish physician and anatomist who was also a bishop, reiterated that fossils were the remains of animals that had once been alive, and correctly suggested that the rock strata containing them must at one time have composed a logical horizontal sequence. These views of Palissy and Steno contained the germ of all later ideas in the science of palaeontology.

But the establishment of palaeontology as a science will always be mainly associated with the name of one man, the great French anatomist Georges Léopold Chrétien Frédéric Dagobert, Baron Cuvier. Cuvier, who was born in 1769, was the son of a retired officer living at Montbéliard between Besançon and Mulhouse in eastern France. He came to Paris as an assistant at the Natural History Museum, and rose to be the foremost figure in French natural science. Apart from his studies of molluscs and the comparative anatomy of fishes, he was greatly interested in fossil bones, of which many gigantic specimens were then being turned up in the quarries of Montmartre. By comparing these bones with those of living species Cuvier came to the extremely important conclusion that fossils represented the remains of extinct races which sometimes resembled, but were yet in many ways different from, the races of animals then alive.

But having arrived at this correct opinion Cuvier found himself in a dilemma. He was strongly opposed to the evolutionary theories of his contemporary Lamarck, who held that species were not fixed and determined for all time but could be gradually modified by their environment. Instead he subscribed to the dogma of the Swedish naturalist Linnaeus, who had declared that 'the existing species of animals are now as they were created in the beginning'. How, then, was he to account for the extinction of some forms of life and the undeniable fact that new ones seemed to have appeared?

His solution of this problem was simple but a trifle naïve. As a good Protestant he naturally accepted the idea of divine Creation, but instead of the generally accepted story told in the

Book of Genesis he proposed that there had been not one Creation but four. The first had been devoted to marine invertebrates and fishes, the second to reptiles, the third to mammals, and the fourth to man. These had occurred successively, but until the fourth Creation, which had produced that nonpareil of virtue the human race, God had been dissatisfied with his handiwork and had ended each episode with a universal cataclysm. Hence the burial of fossils in the various strata of the Earth's crust, and hence, of course, the Biblical Flood, which had formed part of the last cataclysm before man appeared. The theory also conveniently accounted for the chaotic state of the Earth's rocks, which had obviously been several times violently disturbed by convulsions and catastrophes.

. In spite of these magical elements in the cataclysmic theory, it nevertheless helped to establish some extremely valuable ideas. First of these was the fact – previously suggested by Steno – that the rocks of the Earth's surface represented a definite sequence of strata, each determining the length of a particular geological period and each producing its own characteristic assemblage of fossils. The second was that fossils were the remains of real families of animals that could be anatomically described with the same accuracy as living species. And the third was that, in order to give time for the occurrence of four creations and three cataclysms, the Earth must be considerably older than Archbishop Usher had been prepared to allow.

This last point had already been examined by Cuvier's compatriot the Comte de Buffon, and estimates of the Earth's age now varied between forty and eighty thousand years. This was a great improvement on the old time scale, but it was still far from being related to the true facts. The final estimates of the Earth's age originated in the geological discoveries of James Hutton and Sir Charles Lyell. As early as 1785 Hutton had suggested that the erosive agents, such as wind and rain and ice, which were perpetually shaping and reshaping the surface rocks, together with the huge internal pressures responsible for the upraising of mountain ranges, would in themselves be sufficient to account for all the existing geological features of the Earth's crust. This idea was developed

ERA	PERIOD	EPOCH	YEARS AGO IN MILLIONS	AGE OF LIFE-GROUPS
CENOZOIC	TERTIARY	PLIOCENE	15	MAN
		MIOCENE	35	
		OLIGOCENE	45	
		EOCENE	60	
		PALAEOCENE	70	
MESOZOIC	CRETACEOUS		140	LAND PLANTS · SEAWEEDS AND INVERTEBRATE ANIMALS · FISHES · AMPHIBIA · REPTILES · BIRDS · MAMMALS
	JURASSIC		170	
	TRIASSIC		195	
PALAEOZOIC	PERMIAN		220	
	CARBONIFEROUS		275	
	DEVONIAN		320	
	SILURIAN		350	
	ORDOVICIAN		420	
	CAMBRIAN		520	
PROTEROZOIC	PRE-CAMBRIAN			

The Calendar of Earth History. Reproduced from the author's book *A Guide to Earth History*, after Oakley and Muir-Wood. The two parallel lines at the top of the Chart represent the Pleistocene and Holocene Epochs, or Quaternary Period.

by Lyell, who pointed out in his *Principles of Geology* (1830-33) that if the past of the Earth were assumed to be sufficiently long there was no need to postulate cataclysms at all. This theory, which was known as uniformitarianism, was eventually seen to be correct, and it established the amazing fact that the Earth's age must be reckoned not in thousands, but in hundreds of millions of years.

Yet the problem of fossils and of racial extinction still remained. If there were no cataclysms, how could one account for the disappearance of the many thousands of strange species whose fossils had now come to light? This is where the theory of evolution came into its own. As Lamarck had already suggested and Charles Darwin was triumphantly to prove, species are not fixed and unalterable entities but are constantly modified with the passage of time. Through the geological past, from simple beginnings in the seas, life had grown in complexity and diversity until it had reached its highest expression in the advanced mammalian fauna of the present day. The fossils in the rocks therefore represented not mineral freaks of nature, nor yet victims of cataclysm and deluge, but the earlier stages in this grand advance. Among the infinite variety of fossil forms could be found not only the grotesque failures of over a thousand million years of evolutionary experiment, but also the ancestors of all the animals living today, and even of man himself.

We now have a framework which, in association with the chart on the opposite page will enable us to place the subject matter of the next few chapters in its historical setting. We will therefore turn next from general considerations to some of the romantic and entertaining stories of how fossils have been discovered and how their discoverers have succeeded in investing them with life.

CHAPTER SEVEN

The Carcases in the Tundra

Scarce from his mould
Behemoth, biggest born of Earth, upheav'd
His vastness.
                              MILTON: *Paradise Lost*

Lo now, his strength is in his loins, and his force is in the navel of his belly.

He moveth his tail like a cedar: the sinews of his stones are wrapped together.

His bones are as strong pieces of brass; his bones are like bars of iron.
                              JOB: *Ch.* 40. *vv.* 16-18

ONE fact that is clear to every student of palaeontology is that the raw material of his science is almost invariably restricted to the dry bones of formerly living things. It is, in general, his fascinating task to reconstruct from these clues the animal of flesh and blood to which they once belonged, and to bring it imaginatively to life. On very rare occasions, however, and in very special circumstances, he finds that part of his work is already done for him. Not only the bones have been preserved, but also the muscles, flesh and skin – what palaeontologists call the 'soft parts' – so that the animal is revealed exactly as it was in life.

Of the few instances where this has occurred none is more dramatic than the discovery of complete frozen carcases of mammoths in the tundra of Siberia. These huge extinct members of the elephant family roamed across the northern plains of America and Eurasia during the frozen centuries of the Great Ice Age, and with the possible exception of some of the great dinosaurs they seem to have captured the public imagination more than any other species of extinct animal. They also have a particularly interesting and well documented history which gives an idea of the palaeontologist's work at its most rewarding.

As we have already seen, the bones of mammoths were discovered in Europe and interpreted as the remains of dragons or giants long before the existence of completely frozen carcases was even suspected. Huge tusks were also found from time to time, and when not being explained away as the horns of the unicorn or the claws of the griffon, formed a valuable article of trade. Thus in the tenth and eleventh centuries Arab traders used to carry mammoth ivory from the borders of Siberia to Khiva, near the Aral Sea, where it was carved into combs and ornaments and sold at a great profit. The Chinese were also well aware of the existence of the mammoth as early as the fourth century B.C. They apparently believed it to be a living species, describing it as a huge creature with a curved neck and small eyes, 'very stupid and inert'; and for reasons that will appear later they named it the *Fyn shu*, or 'self-concealing mouse'.

Although mammoth bones had been found but not identified in western Europe for many years, Siberian mammoth ivory was not imported here until the early seventeenth century. In 1611 an English navigator named Jonas Logan visited Russia and brought back to London a gigantic tooth which he had acquired from the Samoyedes on the Pechora river. This marked the beginning of a trade in fossil ivory which was later to reach spectacular proportions. At the end of the nineteenth century an average of 50,000 lbs. of mammoth ivory was being sold at the annual market at Yakutsk, and it is estimated that this involved exploiting the remains of between 180 and 200 mammoths a year. During the 300 year occupation of Siberia by the Russians the tusks of at least 45,000 mammoths have been sold in the markets, and this does not include remains which were insufficiently well preserved to have commercial value.

But it is the discovery of the complete carcases of mammoths in the permafrost, or permanently frozen ground, that from a palaeontological point of view provides the most dramatic aspect of the story. As long ago as the seventeenth century reports of mammoth carcases, containing a mixture of fact and legend, were being made by travellers returning from Siberia to civilization. Legends, of course, there were in plenty. The Chinese custom of referring to the mammoth as the 'self-concealing mouse' is suggestive of a belief which was widespread among the tribes of central and northern Asia. The Tartars, for example, maintained that the interior of the Earth was inhabited by gigantic animals who could move about with ease underground, but died as soon as they saw the light of day. Thus mammoth carcases were regarded as the remains of those unfortunate beasts who had lost their bearings in the underworld and accidentally burrowed their way through to the surface. Some authorities even trace the derivation of the word mammoth to the Tartar word for earth, which is reputed to be 'mama'; but caution is necessary here, for this word does not exist in the modern Tartar vocabulary.

The factual part of the story begins in 1692 when Peter the Great, Czar of all the Russias, sent an envoy called Ysbrant Ides to conduct business for him in China. Ides tells how in his travels he fell in with a man who made annual journeys through Siberia for the purpose of collecting fossil ivory. On one of these journeys he had come across the complete head of a mammoth in a piece of frozen earth. The flesh of the head was in a state of decomposition but the bones were still dyed with blood. This story confirmed earlier rumours that gigantic living animals, dark brown in colour and emitting a great stench, inhabited the Siberian tundra.

A few years later another emissary of the Czar brought back a similar tale. His name was Dr D. G. Messerschmidt, and he had been instructed by Peter the Great to study and report on the natural history of Siberia. He learned that in 1724 a Russian soldier had found the head of a mammoth on the banks of the Indigirca river, which flows into the Arctic Ocean in one of the remotest parts of eastern Siberia. This discovery was important not so much for the head itself but for the fact that an eyewitness, a certain Michael Wolochowicz, had found at the same time a piece of skin which was apparently covered with hair. He writes: 'I saw a piece of skin putrefied, appearing out of the side of a sand-hill, which was pretty large, thick-set, and brown, somewhat resembling goat's hair; which skin I could not take for that of a goat, but of a Behemoth, inasmuch as I could not appropriate it to any animal that I knew.'

The word 'Behemoth' in this account refers, of course, to the mammoth; the mammoth and the Biblical behemoth were often identified, and 'behemoth', which is pronounced 'mehemot' by the Arabs, has been regarded by some people as the true original of the mammoth's name. The discovery of hair was significant in suggesting for the first time that the mammoth did not have the comparatively naked skin of the modern elephant but was covered with a long shaggy coat. This was confirmed by later finds and helped naturalists out of a difficult dilemma. Many of them had refused to believe that any animal resembling the tropical elephant could habitually live in northern latitudes. There had even been a tendency to explain away some finds of mammoth bones as the remains of elephants who had become accidentally detached from Hannibal's army and wandered north to destruction in the snows. The hair found on the Siberian carcases removed the necessity for this somewhat unlikely theory and established the mammoth as a legitimate inhabitant of cold climates.

By the end of the eighteenth century the mammoth was generally accepted in systematic zoology as a species of elephant quite different from the two types still living in Africa and India. This was mainly due to the work of the German anthropologist Professor Johann Blumenbach, who in 1799 gave the mammoth the impressive, and still current scientific name of *Elephas primigenius*, or 'first-born elephant'. As we shall see in the next chapter, this estimate of the mammoth's antiquity was a trifle exaggerated, but to Blumenbach must certainly go the credit for putting elephant classification on the right path.

It was not long after the mammoth acquired its scientific identity, that one of the most famous of all frozen carcases was discovered near Cape Bycov at the mouth of the Lena river. The finder was a Tungus chief named Ossip Schumakhof who on a journey along the Lena delta had observed a strange-looking hummock of frozen earth. He had been puzzled by the peculiar contours of the mound, and when he passed that way the following year he kept his eyes open for it. He was astonished to discover that the covering of earth and snow had now partly melted away to reveal a tusk and part of the body of a huge animal. Now the Tungus are a superstitious race, and to touch or even to look at a mammoth carcase is regarded as an extremely dangerous practice. Mammoths, they knew, came from below the ground, the underworld where demons and other powers inimical to man carried on their sinister activities. And Schumakhof recalled that, only a few years before, a Tungus who had had the temerity to interfere with a mammoth carcase had died with all his family. Accordingly he quickly averted his eyes from the carcase with its tempting wealth of ivory, and went on his way to the peninsula of Tarmut. But greed is a potent influence in peasants, as in more sophisticated people, and in succeeding years Schumakhof could not resist passing by his mammoth carcase to see how far it had melted out. The year after the discovery was a hard time in Siberia, and the mammoth was much as it had been before. But the following summer, that of 1803, hot sun had rapidly melted the frozen earth and the corpse had subsided onto a bank of sand lower down. Still Schumakhof could not quite bring himself to touch the now fully exposed body, but in March of the following year temptation proved too strong for him. He returned to the carcase, and probably amazed at his own audacity, cut off the tusks and exchanged them for goods to the value of fifty roubles.

Now it so happened that in 1806 the famous botanist M. F. Adams, a member of the Russian Academy of Sciences, was travelling through Siberia with Count Golovin, the Russian Ambassador to Pekin. He was told of the carcase and set out at once for the Lena delta to examine it. Unfortunately in the interim much damage had been done. Schumakhof had already lined his pockets with the proceeds from the tusks, and the fact that he had not suffered for thus desecrating the corpse had encouraged other Tungus tribesmen to feed its flesh to their dogs in the hard months when meat was short. When Adams arrived on the scene little more than the skeleton was left, and even this lacked one of the forelimbs. Yet the backbone, pelvis, and a shoulder blade were still joined by their ligaments; the skull was covered in macabre fashion with mummified skin, and one of the ears contained a tuft of fried hair. Adams even thought he could distinguish the pupil of the left eye, while dried up remnants of the brain were found in the skull, and the neck was covered by a long, shaggy mane. On the side on which the animal had lain was preserved a patch of hide, still covered with thick hair; it was so heavy that ten men could scarcely lift it. Despite the damage done through putrefaction and the depredations of dogs and wild animals, this was no mean record of an animal that had been dead at least 25,000 years.

It must have been a cause of bitter regret to Adams and his fellow scientists that no qualified person had been able to examine the complete carcase in its original state. If Schumakhof had guarded his secret less well, naturalists would have been able to see the body exactly as it had been buried, a complete and vivid document of a form of life that is now gone from the Earth for ever. As it was, the carcase was the finest that had been discovered to date. Adams packed up such fragments of skin and hair as remained and these found their way eventually into various European museums, including the Zoological Museum in what was then St. Petersburg, and the Museum of the Royal College of Surgeons in London.

During the next ninety years or so reports of mammoths, or portions of mammoths, were frequent from Siberia. But unfortunately news of the few complete specimens never reached a competent authority until it was too late for any but the most fragmentary remains to be salvaged. However, some of the tales of the mammoth hunters, professional and otherwise, make diverting reading. For instance in 1809, three years after Adams had triumphantly returned with his pieces of skin and hair, a Russian government official named Hedenström visited the as yet little known New Siberian Islands. He was not a palaeontologist, but nevertheless could not resist collecting sack-fuls of mammoth bones *en route* with the avowed object of ex-tracting their marrow and turning it into perfume. Unfortun-ately on his return journey he brought the bones into a house where the heat caused the marrow fat to run out onto the floor and become a total loss. Thus, in the saddest fashion, were Russian ladies deprived of this rarest of delights, for which Hedenström had already concocted the market name of *Pommade à Mammouth*.

In 1848 the history of the Siberian mammoths was further enlivened by a hoax. It was reported that a member of a Russian topographical expedition named Benkendorff had come across the complete body of a mammoth floating in a river. The body, we are told, had been eroded from the banks by the swift-flowing current, and only after immense difficulty was it secured by Benkendorff with a rope. But unfortunately the great carcase was bobbing about so violently in the flood that it broke adrift again and vanished for ever from sight. As the less naïve suspected at the time, there was more to this story than met the eye. It transpired that there never had been such an expedition to the area described, and the report was apparently nothing more than an imaginative sketch for a boys' adventure story.

One last mammoth anecdote is perhaps worth putting on record. In 1877 a local chief of police in the Kundat river area near Tomsk transmitted a report to the Russian Academy of Sciences that a carcase, presumed to be that of a mammoth, had been discovered by a peasant in the valley of a small creek known as Nikolka. The Academy immediately equipped an expedition under the direction of the eminent zoologist Polyakov, and despatched it at considerable expense to the scene of the discovery. On his arrival Polyakov was proudly shown a section of mineral aggregate known as 'mountain leather', which had been found 15 feet deep under a gold-bearing layer of sand. The nature of this supposed 'mammoth' was explained to the police chief, who realized at once that a face-saving operation must be conducted without delay. Accordingly he sent for the peasant who had made the original discovery, told him he must take full responsibility, and then confronted him with the now somewhat irate members of the expedition. But questioned once more about his mammoth, the peasant apparently only reaffirmed what he had maintained all along: that he knew his discovery had been a mammoth because he had 'eaten the skin'. When pressed, he merely added: 'seasoned with butter, what is it not possible to eat?' In the face of this irresistible peasant logic neither Polyakov nor the police chief could find anything further to say, and the expedition returned to St. Petersburg poorer in everything but their knowledge of human folly.

But during the period of these abortive investigations many genuine discoveries were also being made. These culminated in 1900 with the most spectacular of all mammoths finds – that of the animal which has since acquired international fame as the mammoth of Beresovka. In the August of that year a Lamut tribesman living near the small Arctic settlement of Sredne-Kolymsk in the north-east of Siberia brought in a mammoth tusk for barter with the local Cossack trader who was named Yavlovksi. During the course of the deal he told Yavloski that he had found the tusk when hunting reindeer and that while searching round for the pair to it had come across the well-preserved head of a mammoth protruding from the ground. This was interesting news, and Yavlovksi had the good sense

4*a*　The Beresovka mammoth, as found in the permafrost of Siberia in 1901

4*b*　The Beresovka mammoth, as restored and mounted in the Zoological Museum at Leningrad

to transmit the story to the Governor of Yakutsk, who in turn sent an urgent message to the Academy of Sciences.

Undismayed by their previous experiences the Academy at once voted a sum of 16,300 roubles, or over £1,500, to enable a party of scientists to examine the carcase. The expedition was placed in the charge of Dr Otto F. Hertz, a zoologist on the staff of the Academy's museum, and within a month it was on its way to Siberia. Accompanying Hertz were the museum's taxidermist, E. W. Pfizenmayer, who has written a most graphic account of his adventures, and a geologist named Sevastianov from Yurievsk University.

The party arrived in Yakutsk in June 1901, and then began an epic journey of 1,500 miles to Sredne-Kolymsk. In summer this part of the country is practically impassable, for sledges cannot be used, and to traverse the thawing tundra on foot or horseback with pack horses to carry the luggage must have been a protracted nightmare. Three months were taken to reach Sredne-Kolymsk, and by the last phase of the journey the geologist was in such a state of exhaustion that some anxiety was felt for his life.

However, the three men arrived safely at their destination and made contact with Yavlovski. Sevastianov being still out of action, Pfizenmayer stayed with him to organize transport for whatever specimens might be obtained, while Hertz set out with Yavlovski for the site. This lay still deeper in the wilds, some 200 miles north-east of Sredne-Kolymsk on the banks of the Beresovka river, and the two men did not arrive there until the third week in September, when winter was already setting in. Yet despite his exhaustion and the absence of his trained assistants, Hertz immediately began the task of excavation.

The body of the mammoth lay in a cliff near the river, and had been partially exposed by a landslide. After a few days careful work a great deal of it was fully exposed and Hertz could see that here, almost within his grasp, was the scientific prize of the age. No other mammoth had ever been found so perfectly preserved. With the exception of the trunk and some flesh on the face which had been eaten by scavenging carnivores the whole carcase was practically intact. Traces of food could still be seen between the massive jaws, and even the contents of the stomach were so fresh that they could be subjected to chemical analysis. Hertz says that the sledge dogs avidly ate portions of the flesh that were thrown to them, while even he himself could scarcely resist tasting a morsel, so succulent and appetizing did it appear.

On October 3rd Pfizenmayer reached the scene of operations with sledges and the rest of the transport equipment. A hut was built over the mammoth remains, which was heated to prevent them from re-freezing, and by October 28th the carcase was completely dismembered and ready for its long journey to St. Petersburg. While the work of dismemberment was going forward several extremely interesting discoveries were made which enabled the scientists to suggest how the mammoth may have met its end. It seemed that the entire cliff region had once rested on a disintegrating glacier in which there were deep crevasses. Above, concealing the crevasses, was a layer of soil which at one time doubtless supported a tundra vegetation on which the mammoths used to feed. The unsuspecting mammoth browsing on the dwarf shrubs had, it seemed, stepped on an area of thin earth concealing a crevasse and had plunged into this natural trap. As an examination of the skeleton revealed, the force of the fall had shattered the pelvis, a forefoot and some of the ribs, and there were indications of a strong internal haemorrhage. The position of the skeleton also suggested how the stricken beast had made its last desperate effort to extricate itself from its tomb. Thus the two forelegs were flexed and appeared to be clutching at the soil in an attempt to raise the creature's vast bulk forward and upward. But its injuries were too serious, and after a few hours hopeless effort it must have slumped back on its haunches and succumbed.

The skeleton of the Beresovka mammoth is now in the Zoological Museum in Leningrad. Alongside, a brilliant reconstruction has been made showing the animal in the exact position in which it was found. This is perhaps the most remarkable palaeontological document in any museum, giving a picture both accurate and dramatic of this sombre incident in the world of over 25,000 years ago.

Since the beginning of the century several further partially preserved carcases have been collected from the Siberian tundra but I have only space to make a brief mention of one. This is not specially interesting scientifically, for it was considerably less well preserved than the Beresovka mammoth, but the story of its recovery had an amusing sequel. First rumours of the mammoth, which was reputed to be situated on the Bolshoi Lyakhov Island of the New Siberian group, came to the ears of C. A. Vollosovich of the Academy of Sciences while he was travelling in the area in 1906. He immediately decided to excavate such remains as could be found, borrowing money from local people to finance the undertaking in the full expectation that the Academy would pay all expenses later on. The remains were located in 1908, and after two years of intermittent excavation the major part of the skeleton and some parts of the carcase were despatched to St. Petersburg. But then came the tiresome but inevitable question of finance. Who was to reimburse the local residents for their outlay in bringing about this successful result? The Academy prevaricated, so that at last in desperation Vollosovich went for help to a wealthy friend of his, Count Stenbok-Fermor. The Count advanced the money without hesitation, but instead of leaving the mammoth in St. Petersburg presented it in 1914 to the Paris Natural History Museum at the Jardin des Plantes. The reason for this generous gift appears to have been somewhat eccentric. Vollosovich stated in a letter to a colleague that the Count had always cherished a desire to have a full public funeral at which a military band was to be an indispensable item. At that time one of the surest guarantees that one would leave the world in this impressive way was to be invested with the *Legion d'Honneur*. Hence the gift to the Jardin des Plantes, which the Count felt would undoubtedly encourage the French government to bestow the decoration, and thereby allow him to make sure of the band. Perhaps few people nowadays would wish to achieve such an object, and certainly not by the purchase of a mammoth, but none can deny that the Count richly deserved to succeed.

Now what of the living mammoth revealed by the Siberian carcases and by the scattered bones found in many different parts of the world? In strict zoological classification there is not one kind of mammoth but three; but the only species we are concerned with here is the famous woolly mammoth of the north which had been named by Blumenbach *Elephas primigenius.* Palaeontologists now know that in its day this mammoth was one of the most widely distributed and successful of all the great mammals of the past. It was found not only in Siberia but throughout the whole of northern Europe, and in many parts of North America as well.

The woolly mammoth lived in what is known as the Pleistocene Epoch of geological time, which lasted from about one million until 10,000 years ago. During this Epoch the northern continents were gripped on four successive occasions by periods of intense cold, which are collectively known as the Great Ice Age. When the climate was at its most severe the great arctic ice sheets reached southward to the Thames, and the now fertile southern counties of England could support only a sparse flora of dwarf shrubs and other tundra vegetation. This tundra fringing the ice sheets was the home of a typical sub-arctic fauna – musk ox, reindeer, arctic fox, wolverine, lemming, giant cave bear – and mammoth.

In summer the tundra was enriched by the hardier grasses which advanced northward from the neighbouring steppes, and these seem to have formed the mammoth's favourite food. We can tell this from the contents of the stomach of the Beresovka mammoth, which included a most interesting assortment of steppe plants. There were seven different kinds of grasses and sedges, as well as thyme, oxtrope, poppies, and even the familiar buttercup. These plants are still found in the Beresovka river region, which shows that for at least part of the Pleistocene Epoch conditions there must have been very like they are today.

When the climate became exceptionally hard the mammoths probably migrated southwards. At these times they came into frequent contact with the early men who during the Ice Age carried on a precarious existence by hunting game in the inhospitable wilderness that was then the European continent. Mammoths must have been a favourite quarry of these prehistoric men. They were caught in pitfalls at fords and other strategic points on the paths of their migrations, and the huge carcases must have made a valuable store of food for many weeks. The capture of these great brutes was not so formidable a task as might be thought. Elephants are still caught today by the primitive method of the concealed pitfall. And, contrary to popular belief, the mammoth was no larger than the elephant (although appearing so by reason of its thick coat).

For many years scientists refused to believe that mammoths and primitive men could have existed in the same environment. According to the rules (and the rules in the early nineteenth century were those laid down in the works of Baron Cuvier) this was a geological impossibility. Between mammoths and men there had been one of those convenient cataclysms so beloved by Cuvier and his faithful followers, which meant that when the first men were created every mammoth had already been engulfed. But then some facts came to light which suggested that perhaps in this instance the rules might be wrong. On the walls of caves in France and Spain were found paintings and engravings by primitive men which showed mammoths, not dead or fossilized, but obviously very much alive.

We now know that these mammoth pictures were indeed the work of our Stone Age ancestors, and played a vital part in their hunting magic. Before going out to trap big game the

Two mammoths drawn by prehistoric man. Left: From a cave wall at Les Eyzies, Dordogne. Right: From an engraving on flat ivory found at La Madeleine, Dordogne. From Windels' *The Lascaux Cave Paintings*

primitive hunters would make an image of their intended quarry in some remote and specially sanctified chamber deep in the hillside. The high priest or 'witch doctor' would then weave a spell round this symbolic representation in the belief that the real animal would likewise be bewitched and fall an easy prey to the hunters.

The hunting of mammoths by primitive man has sometimes been regarded as the main reason for their extinction between 10 and 20 thousand years ago. This does not seem very likely, however, for the human and sub-human population of Europe during the Pleistocene Epoch was extremely sparse. Dense population is impossible in a hunting economy, and the total number of human beings in the whole of Eurasia during the Ice Age was probably less than the numbers living today in any large industrial city. We must remember, too, that although the mammoth was probably regarded by primitive man as a most desirable prize, it was not his main quarry. Horses, reindeer, wild cattle and antelopes were also successfully hunted, and by comparison the inroads made by man on the vast mammoth population must have been almost negligible.

No satisfactory explanation has yet been found for the extinction of this apparently prosperous race. Even a rapidly changing environment, which is often responsible for the depletion of animal populations, cannot be cited in this case; mammoths had already proved their ability to survive the waxing and waning of the different cold periods of the Ice Age, and conditions at the end of the last glaciation, when the mammoth died out, were not vastly different from those of the earlier phases. It seems that the most likely explanation has to do either with some purely physiological factor such as progressive sterility, or even perhaps with the phenomenon known as racial old age. The theory of racial old age suggests that possibly not only individuals but sometimes whole races reach a stage in their development when their vital processes begin to slow up; they have exploited their evolutionary possibilities to the full, and nature with a characteristic lack of sentimentality replaces them with species more fitted to the succeeding stage of development. Such explanations, with some reason, are often dismissed as fanciful. Yet the fact remains that not only the mammoths, but often far vaster assemblages of animals such as the great dinosaurs of the Mesozoic Era, have on occasion been extinguished in a manner that science is at a loss to explain.

Now, after these serious themes, let us end this chapter on a lighter note. Not so very long ago – in the nineties of the last century to be more precise – a strong rumour got about that mammoths were not after all completely extinct. The home of this rumour, not unexpectedly, was North America, where readers of newspapers seem altogether more romantic and less

5   The mammoth, as it appeared in life.
Reconstruction by Maurice Wilson

sceptical than they are on our side of the Atlantic. But the rumour was not entirely the invention of some news-hungry reporter; it had quite an intriguing history which shows how even today legends can spread with a speed and vigour not unworthy of the Middle Ages.

The first stages in the story were innocent enough. A naturalist named Townsend in the employ of the United States Fish Commission was travelling up the coast of Alaska in the U.S. revenue cutter *Corwin*. At one of the stopping places off Cape Prince of Wales some Eskimos brought articles to barter with the ship, including some mammoth ivory. This in itself was not particularly surprising, for during part of the Pleistocene Epoch America and eastern Asia were joined at the Bering Straits, and mammoths could move freely between the two continents. But the sight of the ivory prompted Mr Townsend to show the Eskimos a picture of the Adams mammoth in a book which he had with him, and also to sketch for them a reconstruction of how it may have looked in life. This information was quite new to the Eskimos, and in great excitement they carried off the sketch, and another which they had made themselves, in order to show their friends.

Now everyone likes to be a bearer of news, and the bigger the news the bigger the kudos attached to relating it. Quite naturally, therefore, the pictures came to be regarded not as copies made from a book, but as sketches of real living mammoths which the artists claimed to have seen alive on the Alaskan tundra. Soon the white trappers got hold of the story, the saloons at the trading stations began to hum with rumours, and even the most sceptical backwoodsman when journeying through the Alaskan wilderness found himself casting a quick look over his shoulder now and then.

Further south short paragraphs began to appear in the Press. At first these seem to have attracted only average interest, but then an event occurred which turned the Alaskan mammoths into a nation-wide sensation. In the issue of *McClure's Magazine* for October 1899 a report appeared by a writer called Henry Tukeman describing how, together with a young Alaskan Indian named Paul, he had ventured forth into mammoth country and killed the last surviving mammoth in the world. The story was told in most elaborate detail, even down to a lurid description of the mammoth's last squeals of anger and rage, and the fact that the blast of the rifles pumping bullets into the enraged beast had turned Mr Tukeman deaf for several days. He alleged that he had then returned to the United States and, falling in by chance with 'that generous but eccentric millionaire, Horace P. Conradi,' had persuaded him to purchase the mammoth's remains for a sum running into several millions of dollars. After a long and arduous journey, he said, the hide and skeleton of the enormous brute had been brought back to civilization and were eventually presented by Mr Conradi to America's great national collection, the Museum of the Smithsonian Institution in Washington.

The effect of this last piece of information was spectacular. For many weeks the custodians of the Museum were pestered with letters and telephone calls asking for further information concerning Mr Tukeman's mammoth. Persistent sightseers – some of whom had travelled many hundreds of miles – refused to leave the building until the mammoth, which they believed to have been secreted in the basement, was shown to them. It was often only after protracted argument and the personal assurances of a harrassed curator that they could be reluctantly persuaded that the creature did not exist.

The story was of course a hoax. In the six months' index to *McClure's Magazine* for the period May to October 1899 there is a heading which reads *Fiction: Short Stories;* and below this duly appears *The Killing of the Mammoth* by H. Tukeman. There was, however, no indication on the pages where the story was printed that it did not describe a personal experience of the author's. Thus not for the only time in their history the American public found themselves the victims of an elaborate joke which seems to have provided a great deal of innocent amusement to everyone concerned – except, of course, the long suffering officials of the Smithsonian Museum.

CHAPTER EIGHT

How the Elephant got its Trunk

In the High and Far-Off Times the Elephant, O Best Beloved, had no trunk. He had only a blackish, bulgy nose, as big as a boot, that he could wriggle about from side to side; but he couldn't pick up things with it.

RUDYARD KIPLING: *The Elephant's Child*

> Th'unwieldy Elephant,
> To make them mirth us'd all his might, and wreath'd
> His Lithe Proboscis.
>
> MILTON: *Paradise Lost*

> When people call this beast to mind,
>   They marvel more and more
> At such a LITTLE tail behind,
>   So LARGE a trunk before.
>
> HILAIRE BELLOC: *The Elephant*

AMONG the diverse forms of life, Nature has produced on occasion some amazingly bizarre specializations. Even such comparatively familiar structures as the wings of birds and bats, the long necks of giraffes, and the many-patterned horns of deer and antelopes are, if one stops to consider them, incredibly odd and intriguing inventions. But among these examples of Nature's resourceful imagination it would be difficult to find a more extraordinary yet useful organ than the elephant's trunk.

In the days when the animals were regarded as the product of special creation the explanation of such phenomena did not cause any serious problems. God, as reported in the first chapter of Genesis, was assumed to know best, and any enquiry into the reasons for his mysterious acts was regarded, if not as blasphemy, at least as the height of bad form. But with the arrival of the evolutionists on the scene such an easy escape was no longer possible. If living things, in their infinite variety, were descended from simpler and more primitive ancestors, then science must produce reasons why they had evolved as they had. In meeting this challenge the newly-established

123

science of palaeontology was the evolutionists' main weapon.

The origin of the elephant's trunk is a question that has interested laymen as well as naturalists. In fact curiosity on the subject seems to begin at an early age, as anyone knows who has ever taken a child to the Zoo. We may recall that Rudyard Kipling gave one answer to the inevitable questions that children ask on the subject in the *Just So Stories*. He described how once, long ago, the elephant had no trunk but only a small wriggly nose. Then one day the inquisitive Elephant's Child was seized by a crocodile on the banks of 'the great, grey-green, greasy Limpopo River' of South Africa, and had his nose pulled out into a trunk.

Although palaeontologists are unlikely ever to accept the second part of the story, Kipling was quite right in saying that the first elephant had a nose no bigger than a boot. This was dramatically proved in the first years of this century by the researches of two scientists, Mr H. J. L. Beadnell and Dr C. W. Andrews, in the Fayum district of Egypt. Here, in Eocene strata dating from at least 40 million years ago, they discovered the remains of an ancestral elephant, which in the opinion of many writers was the lineal ancestor of the greater part of the whole elephant order.

The Fayum, or lake province, of Egypt is a depression in the desert to the west of the Nile Valley about 57 miles south of Cairo. The lowest part of the depression is occupied by an expanse of brackish water, which in the Dynastic Period of ancient Egyptian history was used as an artificially-controlled reservoir with the name of Lake Moeris. On the north side of the depression the ground rises in a series of escarpments, and it was this area, consisting mainly of beds of sandstone and clay, that was the source of these first remains of the ancestral elephant.

Andrews named the creature *Moeritherium* after the ancient lake near which it was found. Superficially it bore little relation to later representatives of the order. In size it was considerably smaller than a Shetland pony and the structure of the jaws showed quite clearly that it had had no trunk. It seems to have been a partially amphibious animal, rooting about for its vegetable food along the shores of the warm African lakes and rivers. Probably the animals that most resemble *Moeritherium* today, at least in external characteristics, are the tapirs of Malaya, Central America and Brazil.

Now how do we know that *Moeritherium* was in all probability the forbear of the more recent genera of elephants, or at least very close to the ancestral line? The complete answer to this question would involve us in technicalities of comparative anatomy which it would be tedious to enter into here. But quite apart from this, the connection is shown in a most interesting way by the general appearance of some later fossil forms. There is now, in fact, an almost complete fossil chain connecting *Moeritherium*, or a creature closely resembling it, with the more advanced and specialized elephants of later times.

What happened is briefly this. In the Eocene Epoch, which lasted from about 75 million to 45 million years ago, there seems to have begun a great radiation of elephant types based on different specializations of the primitive *Moeritherium* stock. The starting point of this evolutionary outburst appears to have been East Africa, whence the elephants gradually distributed themselves into nearly every quarter of the globe. As the descendants of the basic stock moved into different environments they evolved in different ways, so that a great multitude of species and sub-species was established. Over three hundred of these are now recognized, ranging from creatures no bigger than a pig to the great imperial mammoth, *Archidiskodon imperator*, which lived in Texas and Nebraska nearly a million years ago.

Among this vast array of elephant species, all but three of which are now extinct, it is of course possible to recognize many different lines of descent. Some of these were widely divergent, while others were sufficiently close together for their representatives to be grouped into a number of natural families. In our quest for the origin of the elephant's trunk two of these groups are particularly important – the true elephants, which include the African and Indian elephants of today, as well as the mammoths and a number of ancestral forms; and the mastodons, which are an altogether more ancient and primitive race. Both these groups are descended from such comparatively small creatures as *Moeritherium*, but they became specialized in different ways and so drew further and further apart.

To see the first stages in the development of the trunk we must look at a very early ancestral mastodon which came from the same Egyptian strata that produced *Moeritherium*. This

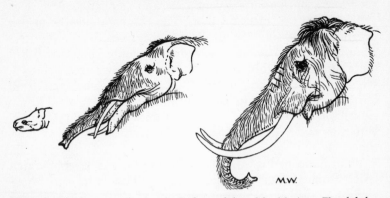

How the elephant got its trunk. Left to right: *Moeritherium, Tetrabelodon,* and *Mastodon americanus*

creature was known as *Palaeomastodon*, or 'ancient mastodon', and its first remains were discovered by Andrews and Beadnell in 1901. They lay in a higher stratum than *Moeritherium*, showing that *Palaeomastodon* had lived at a somewhat later period. It is now known that they belong exclusively to the Oligocene Epoch, which came to an end about 35 million years ago.

This ancestral mastodon was a bigger animal than *Moeritherium*, but an average specimen still only stood about four feet high at the shoulder. What is particularly interesting to our present quest is that there were important changes in the anatomy of the head. In the first place the lower jaw was much elongated and ended in two short tusks like a scoop. The upper jaw was shorter and likewise bore two tusks which curved down towards the lower jaw. The openings in the skull for the nostrils were set much further back in the head than in *Moeritherium*. These factors suggest that *Palaeomastodon* must already have had the beginnings of a trunk which projected just beyond the tip of the lower tusks.

The next stage of development followed in the Miocene Epoch with an extraordinary mastodon called *Tetrabelodon*. In this animal the lengthening of the lower jaw had been carried still further and the upper tusks had grown forward to a roughly equivalent length. We can now also see quite clearly why a trunk was necessary to the animal's survival. Without it *Tetrabelodon* would probably have starved, for all its food and drink would have had to be scooped up with the tusks and tipped or poured laboriously backwards into the mouth. With the trunk, which had become elongated to correspond with the increased length of the lower jaw, the animal could tuck its food away and squirt water down its throat with comparative ease.

Although *Tetrabelodon's* trunk was already quite long the animal itself was still very unlike a modern elephant. The jaws and head were elongated and pointed, whereas the elephant has a flatter, 'bull-dogged' face and a much higher forehead. Also the trunk was still an integral part of the muzzle, running parallel with the lower jaw, and not a free-hanging organ such as was used by the Elephant's Child to spank his uncles and aunts. The development of the free-hanging trunk did not get well under way until the beginning of the Pliocene Epoch, when it became characteristic of nearly all the mastodons, as well as of the true elephants who were evolving at the same time. It was achieved quite simply by a gradual reduction of the lower jaw so that the trunk, which had formerly been a kind of combined lip and nose, eventually hung freely downwards between the upper tusks. The tusks of the lower jaw completely disappeared, and the jaw itself finally receded so far that its relationship with the rest of the skull became comparable to that which exists between the human chin and the remainder of the human face.

Now the reader may well be asking why all these physical changes took place. Obviously they must have been in response to certain problems, and it is interesting to speculate what these problems may have been. It seems that for reasons that are still controversial one of the common general tendencies of evolution is towards increase in size. As the size of the ancestral elephants increased, and their legs became longer and also more pillar-like to hold up the great bulk of their bodies, they apparently found increasing difficulty in reaching the ground to drink and feed. One solution of this problem would have been the evolution of a longer neck, but if this had occurred in such a massive, thickset creature, it would not have been sufficiently rigid to support the weight of the exceptionally heavy head. Hence the neck remained short and the mastodons evolved instead an exceptionally long face and lower jaw. But as we have just seen, this very elongation of the face resulted also in the evolution of the trunk; and once the trunk had evolved, the necessity for an elongated lower jaw was removed, and it gradually receded again. Thus the trunk of the elephants and the later mastodons is seen to be the end-product of a surprisingly intricate process of evolution occupying at least 40 million years of geological time.

Although this really completes the story of how the elephant got its trunk, the mastodons, who were responsible for its early development, are such an interesting group of animals that they deserve a few more words on their own. They are sometimes regarded as the American counterparts of the mammoth, but this is quite incorrect for the two types of elephants were found in both Old and New Worlds. Perhaps the confusion arose from the fact that mastodons became extinct in Eurasia much earlier than in America, where they were certainly contemporaries of Stone Age man. They reached that continent by way of the land bridge that in earlier times connected eastern Siberia with Alaska, and they even penetrated to South America, where Darwin, on his famous voyage in H.M.S. *Beagle*, came across their fossil skeletons.

It is interesting to read in Darwin's journal that the South American natives made exactly the same mistake about the mastodon as had the primitive Siberian tribes about the mammoth, regarding it as a gigantic burrowing animal that lived most of its life underground. There were also current in America, as in Europe, many stories ascribing the fossil remains of mastodons to giants. For example, the first recorded find of American mastodon bones, reported by Cotton Mather in 1714 in the *Philosophical Transactions* of the Royal Society, was interpreted as proving the former existence of a race of gigantic men. It was left to Baron Cuvier to realize the true significance of the American fossils, and it was he also who gave the animal its name of mastodon, or 'breast tooth', from the rounded prominences on the grinders.

The most famous source of mastodon bones in the world is

probably the peat bog known as Big Bone Lick in Kentucky, a few miles south-east of the Ohio river. This was formerly an open lake, but towards the end of the Great Ice Age it gradually became filled with a mass of decaying swamp vegetation which formed a thick floating mat upon its surface. Any mastodon who was unfortunate enough to wander accidentally into this treacherous region quickly sank down into the bog and was suffocated. Over 100 skeletons of the great American mastodon have been recovered from this swamp, together with numerous remains of bison, deer and horses.

The mastodon must have been an exceptionally impressive creature, and Indians living in the region of the Ohio river have numerous legends concerning it. For example, they believe that the skeletons in the Big Bone Lick are the remains of vast herds of mastodons which had formerly ravaged the area and were finally killed by the tribal god with a barrage of thunderbolts. This legend was probably handed down from the ancestors of the tribe, who almost certainly had direct knowledge of the beast. But its capacity for mischief has been exaggerated with repetition, for it was credited with the power to kill the bears, deer and buffalo which the tribe formerly hunted. In actual fact, of course, the mastodon, like the modern elephant, was a vegetarian and probably lived by browsing off the succulent leaves of low bushes.

The great majority of mastodon remains so far discovered are now in museums in the United States. We are fortunate in this country, however, in having a magnificent skeleton in the Natural History collection of the British Museum. This was brought to London in 1843 by none other than the redoubtable Dr Albert Koch, whose exploits with a pseudo sea serpent we have already described in Chapter 2. Koch had excavated the bones in the region of the Missouri river, and the fact that they belonged to different individuals did not deter him from assembling them, with additions from other sources, as a gigantic composite monster with the name of *Missourium*. Koch, as we know, was quite a specialist at this sort of thing, and when he finally brought the monster to England for exhibition at the Egyptian Hall in Piccadilly, Londoners were duly edified to find it had enormous tusks arranged as horns on the top of its head. When he had exploited it to the full he disposed of the bones to the British Museum, and *Missourium*, correctly transformed into *Mastodon americanus*, found its last resting place in the Fossil Mammal Gallery at South Kensington.

So much, then, for the American mastodon, but the history of the primitive members of the elephant family is virtually inexhaustible. Scientific investigators are still trying to decide the relationships of the hundreds of fossil forms found scattered throughout the world, and to unravel the many unsolved problems connected with them. Why, for instance, did the great mastodon *Anancus arvenensis* have long, straight tusks over two-thirds the length of its body? And why did the tusks of the aberrant *Dinotherium* curve right backward and downward like the claws of an enormous cat? But despite such intriguing questions, which cannot yet be answered, palaeontologists have now at least solved the central problem and can tell us with scientific exactness how the elephant got its trunk.

CHAPTER NINE

The Discovery of the Dinosaurs

There were giants in the earth in those days.

GENESIS: *Ch.* 6, *v.* 4

And by the shores of that unwholesome flood
There dwelt the mightiest of the scaly brood;
Huge dragons here indulged their murd'rous bent,
And loathsome lizards frolick'd in the scent
Of fens' most foul effluvium.

SAMUEL MARTINS: *Tartarus* (1709)

'He discovered the Iguanodon'

Inscription on Castle Place,
Gideon Mantell's House at Lewes, Sussex

IN the year 1820 Professor Benjamin Silliman, the famous American chemist and geologist, received a letter from a colleague, Professor Nathan Smith, describing an unusual discovery of fossil bones which had taken place two years previously in the red sandstone of Connecticut. The letter was published in the *American Journal of Science*, of which Silliman was the founder and editor, and it read as follows:

Mr Solomon Ellsworth, Jun. of East-Windsor, (Conn.) has politely favoured me with some specimens of fossil bones included in red sand stone. Mr Ellsworth informs me that they were discovered by blasting in a rock for a well; they were 23 feet below the surface of the earth, and 18 feet below the top of the rock. Unfortunately, before Mr Ellsworth could come to the knowledge of what was going on, the skeleton had been blown to pieces, with the rock which contained it, and several pieces of bones had been picked up, and then lost. The specimens which I have seen are still inclosed in the rock, but from their appearance, it is possible that they are human bones. Mr Ellsworth states that the bones were found in a horizontal position across the bottom of the well, as he thinks nearly to the extent of six feet. It is hoped that the pieces of bones, when they are cleared of the rock which incloses them, will enable us to ascertain the fact whether they are human bones, or the bones of brute animals.

In the following year a further letter was quoted in the *Journal* from a Mr John Hall of Ellington. He mentioned that Dr Porter, 'a respectable surgeon', had been present at the time of the blasting, and was strongly of the opinion that the bones were not human but belonged to an animal about 5 feet long. This was confirmed by a closer examination of the specimens. In particular Mr Hall remarks: 'The *tail* bone was easily discovered by its numerous articulations, distinctly visible when the bones were first obtained, and by its being projected in a curvilinean direction beyond the general mass.'

These brief notes by an American professor and an obscure Connecticut surgeon are the first record in scientific literature of the discovery of that fantastic group of extinct reptiles, the dinosaurs. Unfortunately, however, the investigators had no means of knowing the significance of their find. The bones belonged to a small and comparatively unspectacular species which lived in the Triassic Period before the dinosaurs had finally established their domination of the Earth. Also, as Professor Smith had said, the skeleton had been badly damaged by the blast of the explosion, and it was therefore impossible to give a proper picture of what the animal was like. As has been the case with several other important but unrecognized discoveries, the bone fragments found their way into a drawer in a museum store room and were there quietly forgotten.

The dinosaurs today need little introduction, even to laymen. Over a hundred years ago models of giant dinosaurs by Waterhouse Hawkins were displayed in the grounds of the Crystal Palace at Sydenham, and became a familiar feature of the landscape. Since then such books as Conan Doyle's *The Lost World* and Edgar Wallace's *King Kong* have done much to encourage the dinosaur cult. More recently still dinosaurs have invaded the music hall, the radio and the cinema, while in the United States enterprising advertising agents have found that there is nothing like a *Brontosaurus* to give an impressive aspect to a poster.

In *A Guide to Earth History* I tried to give a picture of the origin and history of this marvellous group of animals. Here, before resuming the story of their discovery, it is only necessary to remind the reader that dinosaurs are reptiles, and that during the Mesozoic Era, which lasted from about 195 million to 75 million years ago they were the most powerful and success-ful animals on the Earth. They ranged in size from small species no bigger than a young kangaroo to gigantic semi-aquatic forms measuring between 80 and 90 feet long and weighing over 40 tons.

America, then, was the scene of the first discovery of dinosaur bones, but the significance of the find was unrecognized and the animals were not correctly identified. The true history of the dinosaurs' discovery can therefore be said to begin in England with an important find which took place near Oxford in the early 1820s. The man responsible for calling attention to this find was the famous British geologist William Buckland, who with typical nineteenth century versatility was also a dean of the church and an expert on agriculture and sanitation.

The site of the discovery was a slate quarry at Stonefield near Woodstock, the source of many of the slates which can be seen on Oxfordshire roofs to this day. In working the quarries vertical shafts had been sunk through a bed of solid rock to a considerable depth, and the fossil remains were embedded in a deep-lying layer over 40 feet from the surface. Buckland de-scribed them in a paper read before the Geological Society of London on February 20th 1824: 'Nothing approaching an entire skelton has yet been found,' he said; 'the detached bones here represented must have belonged to several individuals of various ages and sizes. . . . The vertebral column and ex-tremities much resemble those of quadrupeds, the teeth show the creature to have been oviparous, and to have belonged to the order of Saurians or Lizards.' This identification, which subsequently proved to be perfectly correct, led Buckland to name the owner of the bones *Megalosaurus*, or 'the great reptile', and he accurately assigned it to the Jurassic Period of geological time which ended about 140 million years ago.

Before making his pronouncement Buckland had consulted with Baron Cuvier in Paris, who fully supported the view that here was evidence of the former existence of a gigantic reptile whose remains had been previously unknown to science. One of the thigh bones alone measured 2 feet 9 inches in length and approximately 10 inches in circumference. This fact led Cuvier to declare that the animal must have been over 40 feet long, with a bulk equal to that of an elephant 7 feet high. We now know that these measurements are considerably exaggerated, but *Megalosaurus* was nevertheless quite a sizeable creature, even by dinosaurian standards.

The year following Buckland's paper on *Megalosaurus* another exceptionally interesting find was reported, which perhaps even more than the Oxford bones helped to put dinosaurs on the scientific map. The heroine of this episode was the wife of a country doctor named Gideon Mantell, who practised at Lewes in Sussex. During the summer of 1822 Mrs Mantell had been walking in the Sussex weald in the region of Tilgate Forest between Crawley and Handcross when she had come across a fossil tooth lying by the roadside. Her husband, apart from being a medical man, was a well-known expert on geology and palaeontology, and when he saw the tooth he recognized at once that it was of an extremely novel and interesting kind. Immediately he began an intensive search for further specimens, and was rewarded at length by finding the almost perfect tooth of a young animal as well as a worn stump and several damaged fragments.

We can imagine Mantell seated in the study of his fine white house at Lewes with these enigmatic fossils set out on the desk in front of him. We can imagine, too, his puzzled frown as he tried to decide the kind of animal to which they might have belonged. For this was no ordinary set of specimens; it presented problems that no palaeontologist had yet been called upon to solve. In the first place the teeth showed strong resemblances to the grinding teeth of herbivorous mammals. Yet they had been found in strata which dated from a period long before the first mammals were then believed to have evolved. Could it be that a giant mammal had after all existed in the Mesozoic Era? Or did the teeth date from more recent times, having been accidentally washed into the Wealden strata by the current of some ancient stream?

Mantell was completely baffled by these problems, and his scientific colleagues were unable to give him very much assistance. Eventually he forwarded the teeth to the eminent geologist Sir Charles Lyell in the hope that he might be able to throw some light on the matter. Lyell seems to have been as mystified as everyone else, but he nevertheless decided that the teeth were so interesting that he despatched them forthwith to Paris for the opinion of Baron Cuvier. There followed a few weeks of suspense while the great man deliberated. Then back came the answer: they were probably the incisor teeth of an extinct rhinoceros, or even perhaps of a giant fish.

But this unexpected verdict still did not satisfy Mantell. He put his precious teeth in a case and took them to the Royal College of Surgeons in London to enlist the aid of William Clift, the Keeper of the Hunterian Museum. For many long hours Clift and he went round the collections comparing the teeth with those of every animal, likely or unlikely, to which they might bear some resemblance. As the afternoon wore on they became more and more depressed, for nowhere did there seem to be any sign of what they were after. At last the time came for Mantell to take his leave, once again baffled and disappointed. But just as he was on the point of going Clift asked him if he would like to see the model of the strange New World lizard known as the iguana which had recently been mounted for the Museum by Samuel Stutchbury of the Bristol Institution. The two men were admiring the exhibit when Mantell suddenly lent forward with an excited exclamation. Here, in the mouth of the iguana, were teeth that were virtually miniature replicas of those he still carried in his hand.

Immediately Mantell prepared a paper to make known his discovery to the scientific world. Undismayed by a new opinion from Cuvier that perhaps after all a hippopotamus might be the most likely owner of the teeth, he accepted an invitation from Davies Gilbert, Vice-President of the Royal Society, to lay before the Society his own views on the matter. In a famous paper communicated on February 10th 1825 he asserted that the teeth belonged not to a mammal, but to a new species of fossil reptile which had lived in England over 120 million years ago. At the suggestion of the geologist William Conybeare he named it *Iguanodon* to show its relation to the iguana which had enabled him to bring his search to a successful end.

In fairness to Cuvier it must be added that he withdrew his former identification and unreservedly accepted the opinion of Mantell. In this he showed a humility and scientific integrity that was fully worthy of his great reputation. But although the reptilian character of *Iguanodon* had now been established, its skeletal anatomy was still completely unknown. The first knowledge of this came with the discovery in May 1834 of numerous bones of the animal in a stone quarry belonging to a Mr W. H. Bensted of Maidstone. From these and other later finds it was deduced that *Iguanodon* must have been a truly gigantic animal, sometimes measuring as much as 30 feet in length. Its shape was generally lizard-like but it walked erect on its hind legs and carried its head about 15 feet from the ground. Although so huge, it was, as its teeth showed, a harmless planteater which lived by browsing along the banks of the great river delta which covered the present Sussex Weald during the Cretaceous Period.

Mantell himself has drawn an evocative picture of the strange primeval landscape in which *Iguanodon* made its home. 'That country', he writes, 'must have been diversified by hill and dale, by streams and torrents, the tributaries of its mighty river. Arborescent ferns, palms and yuccas, constituted its groves and forests, delicate ferns and grasses, the vegetable clothing of its soil; and in its marshes, equiseta, and plants of a like nature, prevailed. It was peopled by enormous reptiles, among which the colossal Iguanodon and the Megalosaurus were the chief. Crocodiles and turtles, flying reptiles and birds, frequented its ferns and rivers, and deposited their eggs on the banks and shoals; and its waters teemed with lizards, fishes and mollusca.'

By 1841, when Sir Richard Owen first coined the word dinosaur, or 'terrible reptile', to describe such gigantic animals, *Iguanodon* was already well established as the most famous member of the group. In the following decade, a year after Mantell's death, its reputation was still further augmented in a rather peculiar way. At this time the Crystal Palace grounds at Sydenham were adorned with gigantic reconstructions of dinosaurs by Waterhouse Hawkins. This gentleman seems to have possessed both a sense of humour and a good eye for publicity. While the reconstructions were still being made, several eminent scientific gentlemen, including Sir Richard Owen, Professor Edward Forbes, and the ornithologist John Gould, were delighted to receive an invitation to the Crystal Palace to inspect the progress of the work. The invitation was written on the wing of a pterodactyl, a circumstance prophetic of what was to follow. Twenty-one acceptances were received and on December 31st 1853 the guests arrived at the appointed hour

6a   *Megalosaurus*, the 'great fossil lizard of Stonesfield'.
Reconstruction by Maurice Wilson

6b   *Iguanodon*, a giant vegetarian dinosaur that lived in Sussex about 100 million years ago. *Reconstruction by Maurice Wilson*

to find a splendid dinner laid out *inside* the body of the *Iguanodon*. In addition, as was obviously inevitable, there was a reporter and draftsman from the *Illustrated London News* to take a detailed account of the affair. This duly appeared in the following issue,

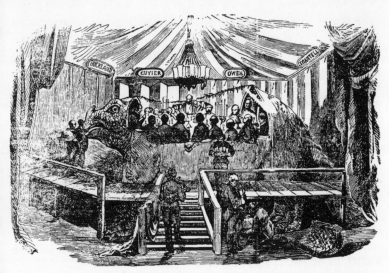

Professor Owen dining in the *Iguanodon* model at the Crystal Palace, Sydenham. From *The Illustrated London News*, January 7th 1854

and an illustration showed Owen at the head of the table delivering a eulogy on Buckland, Cuvier, Mantell and the other pioneers whose work had led to the dinosaurs' discovery. 'After several appropriate toasts,' concludes the *Illustrated London News*, 'this agreeable party of philosophers returned to London by rail, evidently well pleased with the modern hospitality of the Iguanodon, whose ancient sides there is no reason to suppose had ever before been shaken with philosophic mirth.'

Since these spirited times our knowledge of *Iguanodon* has been greatly increased by numerous important finds. Outstanding among these was the discovery in 1878 of the remains of no less than 29 skeletons in a coal mine at Bernissart in Belgium. The majority of the skeletons were complete down to the last bone, and a cast of one of them is now among the most impressive exhibits in the Dinosaur Gallery at the British Museum (Natural History). Alongside it is another skeleton of an *Iguanodon* of a somewhat smaller kind. This was obtained in 1925 from the debris of Wealden shales after a fall of the cliff near Atherfield in the Isle of Wight, and is interesting as belonging to an entirely new species.

In North America, after the first unrecognized find of dinosaur bones in Connecticut, little of importance occurred until 1858. In this year a Mr William Foulke, a member of the Academy of Natural Sciences of Philadelphia, happened to be passing the summer and autumn at Haddonfield in Camden County, New Jersey. Now Haddonfield in those days was quite a small village and it was natural that when Mr Foulke dropped into the local inn to refresh himself he should also pick up a good deal of the gossip of the neighbourhood. As an amateur of science one item that particularly interested him concerned a local farmer named John Hopkins, who twenty years previously had dug up some large bones from a marl pit in one of his fields.

Twenty years is quite a long time and Mr Foulke had little hope of being able to run the bones to earth. But he nevertheless called at Mr Hopkins' farm to make enquiries. There he learnt, as he had feared, that the farmer had been a young man at the time of the discovery and, being little interested in the bones, had allowed souvenir hunters to carry them away. However, when Foulke had explained to him their possible importance to science, he showed himself very willing to co-operate in a new search. With some difficulty the site of the old marl pit was located and diggers were set to work. Within a few days they were rewarded by finding at a depth of between 9 and 10 feet a large number of bones that had survived the former excavations.

Mr Foulke's report of the find, as made later to the Academy, shows the great efficiency with which he went about his task: 'The marl being tenacious', he said, 'great care was requisite to extricate the fossils. With a small trowel and a knife, the bones were carefully dissected from their bed and from one another. A sketch was made of their position, and some measurements were taken of them, in anticipation of the contingency of their fracture in the attempt to remove them. . . . Each bone was separately transferred to a board, and thus carried from the pit, and then wrapped in a piece of coarse cloth.

Thus enveloped it was laid upon a thick bed of straw in the bottom of a cart; and the whole was safely transported in this way, about three quarters of a mile, to my residence.'

Fortunately, as Foulke himself might have expressed it, the fracture of the bones was not a contingency that eventuated, and the specimens were safely delivered into the hands of Joseph Leidy, the famous professor of anatomy in the University of Pennsylvannia and founder of vertebrate palaeontology in America. By this time, of course, through the discovery of *Megalosaurus* and *Iguanodon* in England, the existence of the Mesozoic dinosaurs was an established fact. Leidy therefore had little difficulty in identifying the bones as belonging to another of these gigantic reptiles. He declared it to be a representative of an entirely new genus, for which he proposed the name *Hadrosaurus foulkii*, or 'Foulke's bulky reptile'.

Hadrosaurus foulkii, the duck-billed dinosaur found at Haddonfield, New Jersey, in 1858. *Reconstruction by Maurice Wilson*

Hadrosaurus belonged to the extraordinary family of the duck-billed dinosaurs, which enjoyed their heyday during the Upper Cretaceous Period between 90 million and 70 million years ago. It was related, although not closely, to *Iguanodon*, and was chiefly remarkable for its extraordinary toothless bill. In size it was comparable to *Iguanodon* – between 20 and 30 feet long – and was likewise a harmless browser living on the succulent vegetation of the tropical swamps, which at that time extended far north into temperate America.

After the discovery of *Hadrosaurus* there were no really spectacular developments until the 1870s. But then began two decades of intense activity which resulted in the discovery of an array of gigantic dinosaurs whose former existence had never even been suspected. This period was also marked, or marred, by one of the most savage feuds in scientific history: the struggle for pre-eminence between two rival professors – Edward Drinker Cope of Philadelphia and Othniel Charles Marsh of Yale.

Both Cope and Marsh were men of means, and both had risen to eminence in the science of vertebrate palaeontology. Their relations never seem to have been cordial, and when circumstances eventually brought them into direct competition the result was a war of attrition, prosecuted with the most implacable violence on either side. The immediate cause of this conflict was the discovery in the western United States of a series of beds of fossil bones which promised to be the richest ever investigated. These had come to light through the work of the newly established U.S. Geological Survey, which was at this time making the first scientific investigation of the Western Territories.

So far as dinosaurs were concerned, Cope was first in the field. In 1876 he led an expedition to the Judith river badlands of Montana, an area where fossils had previously been noted by the geologist Ferdinand Hayden, but never investigated due to the activities of Blackfoot Indians. (It must be remembered that these were the days of the now legendary 'Wild West', when the wars of cowboys and Indians were not confined to celluloid strips, and even palaeontologists ventured forth with a geological hammer in one hand and a loaded rifle in the other.) After a hard and dangerous journey Cope was rewarded by the discovery of the teeth and bones of over a score of different species of dinosaurs. He also collected an almost complete skeleton of the extraordinary horned dinosaur known as *Monoclonius crassus*.

This was an impressive haul, but Professor Marsh was not slow in retaliating. As early as 1868, when he had made his first transcontinental journey, he had suspected that formations in the Rocky Mountain region might be a profitable hunting ground for fossils. Three years later, while on the second of two expeditions sent out by Yale University, he had collected the greater part of a 15 foot dinosaur skeleton from western Kansas. He therefore concentrated most of his energies on this area, and in 1877 – the year following Cope's trip to Montana – the first consignment of fossil bones reached him from the now famous Morrison formation of Colorado. Among these was the left femur of a gigantic dinosaur which Marsh estimated to have measured at least 50 feet long, making it the largest land animal thus far discovered. This dinosaur, which was given the name of *Atlantosaurus*, is now known to have been a giant amphibious form closely related to the well-known *Brontosaurus*.

Professor Marsh's Primeval Troupe. A cartoon that appeared in *Punch*, September 13th 1890. (Reproduced by permission of the Proprietors.)

The battle between Cope and Marsh was now well and truly joined. For the next twenty years the main object of each party seems to have been to keep his discoveries secret until the last possible moment. In order to achieve this end, the whereabouts of every locality was jealously concealed until the cream of its fossil remains had been extracted. Poaching, of course, was rife, and secrecy was made doubly difficult by the fact that each professor hired parties of collectors in the field who changed their allegiances according to the pay offered and the terms they were on at any given time with their respective employers.

It would be impossible here to give even the briefest summary of the puerile stratagems to which these two distinguished men were prepared to resort to discredit each other's finds and to establish a valueless priority; it is one of the most sordid and discreditable tales in the annals of science. At the same time we must recognize that both Cope and Marsh had a competence and brilliance that have seldom been surpassed. In spite of their rivalry, or perhaps even because of it, the world was presented in a few short years with a comprehensive and enthralling picture of life in that distant period when these extraordinary reptiles were the rulers of the Earth. Two great fossil collections were built up and many dozens of new and spectacular species were faithfully examined and described. Thus Cope and Marsh completed the work begun fifty years earlier by Buckland and Mantell, and revealed for the first time the amazing diversity of the dinosaur group. In their lifetimes they may have presented the sorry spectacle of two dogs senselessly fighting over the same bone, but at least the bone was a worthy prize, which, in spite of their quarrels could be preserved for posterity in America's great national museums as dramatic evidence of the life of the past.

CHAPTER TEN

The Footprints at Carson City Gaol

There on the naked stone remained the tracks
Where first the sea-beasts crawled out of the sea,
A few salt yards upon the long dark trail
That led through aeons to the tidal roar
Of lighted cities and this world of tears.
> ALFRED NOYES: 'The Testimony of the Rocks',
> from *The Torch Bearers*

'Tracks,' said Piglet. 'Paw-marks.' He gave a little squeak of excitement. 'Oh, Pooh! Do you think it's a – a – a Woozle?

'It may be', said Pooh. 'Sometimes it is and sometimes it isn't. You never can tell with paw-marks.'
> A. A. MILNE: *Winnie-the-Pooh*

JUST over a mile outside Carson City, the capital of the State of Nevada, is a large stone building – the State Penitentiary. Nearby is a quarry, the source from which the stones of the building have been cut, and a number of warm springs, or geysers. This prison has several unusual claims to fame. For example, the more ghoulish sightseer can read in the guide book that it was the first prison in the United States to install a lethal gas chamber for the infliction of the death penalty; and if he wishes he can inspect the old execution chair, with its gun-rests in front of it, where in early days the accused, if he so preferred, could invoke the alternative of being shot instead of hanged. But to those whose tastes are less macabre Carson City gaol is chiefly remarkable as the site of a number of famous fossil footprints, whose discovery caused one of the most entertaining scientific rumpuses of the nineteenth century.

To set the scene of the story we must go back over a hundred years to the time when Carson City was founded. In those days it was simply a small trading station consisting of a store and a few shacks and tents – a tiny outpost of commercial enterprise in the as yet unexplored and unexploited wilderness of the Wild West. At the end of the Civil War, however, the government of the United States began a great drive to open up the

Western Territories. The wagons began to roll along the Californian trail, and when gold and silver were found in the Rocky Mountains it seemed for a time that Carson City might become a great and flourishing provincial centre. But the resources of the local mines proved limited, and after an initial period of excitement the township relapsed into comparative obscurity. Those who remained there were mostly men who had abandoned the mad rush for gold, and had settled down in this beautiful valley to make a permanent home with their wives and families. By 1900 the population had dwindled to just over 2,000, and even today it has only grown by a few hundreds, the majority of the inhabitants being miners or employees of the Virginia and Truckee railway whose repair shops are in the town.

When Nevada's first Territorial Legislature was formed in the 1850s one of Governor Nye's first acts was to declare Carson City the state capital. And as the capital, it had obviously to be the seat of the state prison. Fortunately suitable premises were not difficult to find: an enterprising frontiersman named Abe Curry, who had made his pile in gold, obligingly offered to rent out part of an hotel he had built for the reception of the prisoners. This was at Warm Springs, just outside the city boundaries, and not the least of its qualifications as a prison was that it was one of the few buildings in the whole of the Western Territories that was provided with solid stone walls. In addition, although it is doubtful if the prisoners ever felt the benefit of this advantage, the hotel is said to have boasted the only bath house within a radius of 250 miles.

Warm Springs Hotel – or the Hotel de Curry as it was affectionately known to the citizens of Carson – served its new function admirably. In fact it soon became so crowded with prisoners that no room was left for the legitimate guests, and in 1864 it was purchased outright by the Legislature for 75,000 dollars. Thereafter the prison went from strength to strength. Additions and alterations were made, and modernizations carried out to bring the rest of the premises into line with the bath house. Finally, during blasting operations in the nearby quarry for stone for one of these improvements, the discovery was made that was to confer upon Carson City gaol the crowning glory of international fame.

One morning, before laying their charges of dynamite, some

workmen were clearing rubble and surface dirt from a part of the quarry when one of them noticed imprinted on sandstone below the superficial deposits a number of marks that looked like animal tracks. He called the attention of his workmates to these and they all began an inspection of the nearby ground. It soon became apparent that the whole area was covered with the footprints of a variety of animals, ranging from the paw

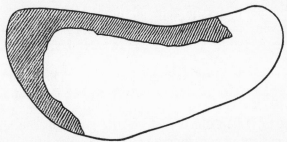

One of the Carson footprints (shaded portion restored by Dr W. H. Harkness). From the *American Journal of Science* (1883)

marks of a dog-like creature to some huge imprints like those of elephants. Finally an even more dramatic discovery was made – a number of large impressions 18 inches long by 8 inches across, which strongly resembled the footprints of gigantic men.

It is not difficult to imagine the stir caused in Carson City by these strange happenings at the Hotel de Curry. The saloons buzzed with rumours and speculations and everyone in the county, whether qualified or not, was called upon to express an opinion. Articles appeared in the local Press and were copied by the larger journals of the Pacific Coast. Eventually the storm reached the California Academy of Sciences, whose members found themselves split into two violently opposed factions. Human, or not human, was the great question, and each side had its passionate adherents. Finally every scientific society in America, and indeed in the world, had heard of Carson City and its famous footprints, and was ready to defend its views with the most cogent of learned arguments.

At the height of the storm an article appeared in the Sacramento *Daily Record-Union* over the name of Mark Twain. This maintained, in mock serious vein, that far from being the work of prehistoric man, or even of the giant cave bear or the Irish elk, the tracks had been made by the Carson City Legislature at the time of their adjourmnent. 'It had rained all the evening outside,' he wrote, 'and it had rained whiskey all the evening inside. . . . It was then that they made the tracks. . . . I was there and I saw them march. The primeval man was absent; the Irish elk did not arrive; the cave bear responded not to the summons. . . . The menagerie was entirely local.'

The human tracks, he went on, must have been made by the Speaker who never wore shoes and whose feet had obviously become enlarged to enormous size through being clogged with mud and straw. As for the Irish elk theory it could be dismissed for the most valid of geological reasons. 'The Irish', wrote Mark Twain, 'are a comparatively recent formation. They belong in the old blue grindstone Tertiary, and are there confined to the stratified rocks of the post-Pliocene alluvium and upper Pentamenus limestone. The assertion of Hugh Miller and other early observers, that traces of them are discoverable in the Jurassic deposits of the Carboniferous chalks, between the median layer of old basaltic gneiss and the marsupial crinoids of the Palaeozoic conglomerate was regarded with suspicion at the time and is now known to have been wholly bituminous.' This satirical parody of scientific jargon seems to have ended the Carson footprint controversy once and for all.

The correct explanation of the tracks was, in fact, quite simple, and was given by Professor Marsh in a paper read before the National Academy of Sciences in New York in 1882. The smaller footprints, he said, were the work of deer, horses, and wolves; the elephant-like footmarks had been left by a mastodon; and the supposed human footprints belonged in reality to a gigantic extinct ground sloth known as *Mylodon*. Marsh estimated the age of the tracks at about a million years, and it is now generally assumed that they were made on the sandy shore of an ancient lake which formerly occupied a depression in this part of Nevada.

Although the Carson footprints were the cause of so much excitement and publicity they are by no means unique, and are not even the most impressive example of this kind of fossil-ization. Perhaps the most interesting of all fossil trackways are those preserved in the red sandstone of the Connecticut Valley.

Here there are innumerable footprints of Triassic dinosaurs and other early reptiles which have been exhaustively described by James Deane, R. S. Lull, and other authorities. Another dramatic series, suggesting how a giant herbivorous dinosaur was pursued by a smaller carnivorous species, is known from Lower Cretaceous strata near Glen Rose in Texas, while in several other parts of America the rocks bear clear imprints of mammals, birds, amphibians, and even fishes and invertebrates. The fish 'tracks' consist of fin imprints probably made by individuals who became stranded in the shores of drying pools, while the claw marks of an early species of horseshoe crab were for many years a baffling problem to palaeontologists. In Europe also numerous fossil footprints have been found. Germany, as we shall shortly see, was the site of a particularly interesting series, while the tracks of tortoises in Cheshire have at different times been interpreted as the marks made by members of Noah's family or as footprints left behind by the devil.

In many ways the tracks made by animals who lived perhaps over 100 million years ago are more moving and significant than the best preserved set of fossilized bones. We seem to approach closer to the living creature, trailing it as we might follow the spoor of an animal alive today. Sometimes it is possible to reconstruct from such fossil evidence a great deal of the life activities of species now long extinct. For example, we can watch the progress of a dinosaur along the shore of an ancient swamp, following its every twist and turn, seeing where it faltered or slipped, and where it paused to rest, the imprint of its tail being permanently fixed in the solidifying mud. Sometimes, too, we can see where a sudden storm overtook the scurrying animals, the sand being pitted with the marks of raindrops. Such evidence now comprises the raw material of a special science, the science of ichnology, which deals exclusively with what Dr G. G. Simpson has aptly called 'fossilized actions'. This science enables us to deduce not only the stride and stance of many species of ancient animals, but also their gait, their speed of travel, and even their approximate weight and height.

In spite of the fact that fossil trackways are by no means uncommon, various rather special conditions had to prevail before they could be preserved. The first requirement was that the animal should walk across an expanse of sand that was sufficiently soft to retain the imprint of its feet, yet not so soft that the print should vanish after the animal had gone. Next there had to be a period of drought so that the imprint would harden into semi-permanent form in the sun-baked sand. And finally it had to be covered by new wind-blown deposits to protect it from the erosive action of the weather. If these conditions were fulfilled the track often looks as clear today as it did a minute or two after the animal had passed.

And now, to conclude, I would like to tell the story of an animal which is known to scientists entirely from the kind of fossil trackways we have just described. Not a single bone of this animal's skeleton has yet come to light, and except for its

footmarks we have no clues of any kind to help us decide what it was like. It is known by the scientific name of *Chirotherium*, and for over a century it has been the subject of much detailed research and speculation. In fact, it is the classic example of the contribution made by ichnology to our knowledge of the past.

The first footprints of *Chirotherium* were observed in 1834 at the village of Hessburg, near Hillburghausen in Saxony, and were described by Professor F. K. L. Sickler in an open letter to Professor Blumenbach of the University of Göttingen. The footprints were imprinted in deep red sandstone and were of the striking appearance represented in the accompanying illustration. The marks of the forefeet were 4 inches long by 3 inches wide, and those of the hind feet about twice those measurements. The reason why the creature was named *Chirotherium*, or 'hand-beast', is immediately apparent, for each footprint, and especially the larger ones of the series, is an almost exact replica of the print that would be made by a human hand.

As time went on similar tracks were found in different parts of Europe, including some excellent examples from England. Although there were differences in size, and occasionally

The footprints of *Chirotherium*. From Owen's *Palaeontology* (1861)

in detail, suggesting that there was more than one species of *Chirotherium*, all the tracks manifestly belonged to the same type of animal. A particularly puzzling feature was that they were always arranged in pairs in a single line, the small print slightly in front of the large one, with the thumb pointing alternately to left and right in each pair.

But if exact knowledge of *Chirotherium* was wanting, there was no shortage of theories. In the year following Sickler's open letter it seems to have been almost a point of honour with palaeontologists to launch forth into print with some kind of pronouncement on the subject. Later, as more and more tracks came to light, the original theories were amplified or changed, and these enigmatical footprints became the subject of a whole library of monographs by their learned students.

Dipping into this voluminous literature, it is interesting to note the many different types of creature with which *Chirotherium* has been identified. One of the first guesses was that it may have been a giant ape, but this does not seem to have aroused enthusiasm in any quarter. Professor Kaup, who had first coined the name *Chirotherium*, suggested that the animal might be allied to the marsupials, basing this identification on the fact that in kangaroos the first toe is likewise set at an angle in relation to the others and there is a similar disproportion between the fore and hind feet. Rival theories mentioned crocodiles, mandrills and giant toads, while one authority actually went so far as to propose that the large tracks were those of the giant cave bear, *Ursus spelaeus*, while the smaller were those of a large monkey. What he did not explain, however, was why these two animals should have been so enamoured of each other that one always followed in the other's tracks.

The unusual outward pointing position of the 'thumb' was one of the main stumbling blocks to every explanation, and was perhaps most ingeniously dealt with in a contribution from Sir Richard Owen. Owen carefully studied every theory so far put forward, and re-examined the fossil evidence. He then prepared a reconstruction based on all the available data, which was published to the world in 1851 in the third edition of Sir Charles Lyell's *Manual of Geology*. The reconstruction resembled (in so far as it could be said to resemble anything at all) a cross between a long-legged crocodile and a gigantic frog. To explain the thumbprints Owen suggested that the creature must have walked by crossing one leg over the other, so that at each step the left foot was placed to the right of the right foot. Accompanying Lyell's text was the illustration which I re-

Chirotherium, as reconstructed from its tracks by Sir Richard Owen. From Lyell's *Manual of Geology* (3rd Edition, 1851)

produce above. It shows the tottering *Chirotherium* literally making tracks, regarding the reader the while with an apprehensive stare. The creature's dismay would seem to be well-founded when one reflects on the hazards of this unorthodox mode of progression.

Despite Owen's almost legendary reputation, his reconstruction seems to have obtained little favour, and in the sixth edition of Lyell's book it was tactfully dropped. However, it did finally establish in scientific thought the important possibility that *Chirotherium* might after all be a reptile. In fact there was a movement to change the second part of the name from *therium*, which means 'beast' and in scientific nomenclature is usually reserved for mammals, to *saurus*, which means 'lizard' and is commonly used in the general sense of 'reptile'. As it transpired, the change would have been an exceedingly fortunate one, for *Chirotherium* was eventually proved to be reptilian; but by the time this was realized the old and inaccurate name was already too well established to be replaced.

The man finally responsible for clearing up the *Chirotherium* problem was the German palaeontologist Wolfgang Soergel. His findings were published in 1925 in a book called *Die Fährten der Chirotheria* which is a masterpiece of scientific deduction from what were seemingly the slenderest of clues. The reptilian nature of the beast had already been proved by the discovery of the imprint of scales associated with one of the tracks, but Soergel was able to go much further than this general identification. Taking as the main subject of his disquisition the relatively large species of *Chirotherium* known as *Chirotherium barthi*, he worked out its description and some of its habits with an acumen worthy of Sherlock Holmes.

He began by pointing out that the position of the thumbprints had always been an unnecessary source of confusion. Many reptiles have one of the five digits pointing away from the remainder on the *outside* of the foot. This is of course the reverse of the arrangement found in man and in other members of the order Primates, where the thumb and big toe are on the inside. Moreover Soergel could point to a close parallel with *Chirotherium* in a species of fossil reptile that was already known from its bones. This was the creature known as *Euparkeria capensis*, a small Triassic form from South Africa belonging to a group known as the Pseudosuchia, or 'false crocodiles', which was ancestral to the dinosaurs.

Soergel also made a careful study of the relative depth of the prints of the fore and hind limbs in the *Chirotherium* tracks. He found that whereas the hind limbs were usually deeply impressed in the ground, the smaller front limbs made a much lighter impression, and were sometimes entirely absent. This suggested that the creature carried most of its weight on the hind limbs, and may occasionally have walked on these alone in the manner of the bipedal dinosaurs. But if this were so, he argued, the weight of the body must have been more or less evenly distributed fore and aft of the hind legs. This would have necessitated a fairly long and heavy tail to counterbalance the weight of the head, neck, and foreparts. For the same reason the neck would probably have been comparatively short.

So far so good, but how about the creature's size and habits? The length of stride suggested a body length of about three feet and, for the reasons outlined above, the tail must have been at least equally long. Adding eighteen inches or so for the neck the total length would have been from seven to eight feet. On some of the tracks there was a faint suggestion of claws, but these seem generally to have been carried so that they were protected from contact with the ground. Soergel deduced from this fact that *Chirotherium* was in all probability carnivorous.

The monograph included several other suggestions of a more speculative character, but we already have an amazingly complete picture of the kind of animal that made the hitherto mysterious tracks. It was a smallish reptile, almost certainly a member of the Pseudosuchia, and therefore probably ancestral to several species of Mesozoic dinosaurs. It had a body and tail of about equal length, a short neck, and the fairly large head of a typical carnivore. The hind part of the body was more massive than the front, and the animal sometimes walked on the hind legs alone. The genus to which it belonged was represented by a number of species, some larger than others, the later forms seeming to have progressed further towards a bipedal gait than the earlier ones. Several species were quite common in Europe during the Lower Triassic period between 195 million and 185 million years ago, while in the area now occupied by the British Isles they persisted for a further 15 million to 20 million years. A related form was also found in America.

The illustration shows a reconstruction of what *Chirotherium* was probably like, based on these deductions by Wolfgang

Chirotherium, as reconstructed from its tracks by Wolfgang Soergel. From *Die Fährten der Chirotheria*

Soergel. When we reflect that the only clues he had to go on were a few footprints made on damp sand by an animal that has been extinct for over 170 million years we may perhaps understand some of the interest and fascination of the science of ichnology.

PART THREE

Living Links with the Past

CHAPTER ELEVEN

The Fossil that Came to Life

Unde etiam vulgare Graeciae dictum 'semper aliquid novi Africam adferre'.

PLINY: *Historia Naturalis*

Where hast thou floated, in what seas pursued
Thy pastime! when wast thou an egg new-spawn'd
Lost in th'immensity of ocean's waste?

COWPER: *Verses sent to William Unwin* April 1784

THE first part of this book dealt with the natural history of the various mythical animals that were once thought to inhabit the Earth; the second with some of the real monsters of the past, and the methods which led to their discovery. In Parts 3 and 4 I should like to bring the reader back once more to recent times to discuss, firstly, some of those famous survivals of the past generally known as 'living fossils' and, secondly, a few of the more interesting species of animals that have become extinct during the historic period.

The term 'living fossil' was coined by Charles Darwin to describe a species of ancient tree known as *Ginkgo biloba*, but it is now applied to any form of life that has survived unchanged, or almost unchanged, from a remote period in the geological past. Taken literally, of course, the expression is a meaningless contradiction, the very essence of a fossil being that it is not alive. But it is a convenient and descriptive term, and until someone thinks of a better one it will doubtless continue to be used.

The first question we must ask concerning living fossils is why certain forms of life should persist for long periods while others either change or die out. To answer it we must make a brief reference to the mechanism of organic evolution. In the ordinary way, of course, constant change is taking place in the form and behaviour of living things. This culminates eventually in the production of new genera and species, each specialized in different way yet able to trace back its origin at some stage to a common ancestor. Geologically speaking new genera and species can be produced in a comparatively short space of time. Thus the genus *Homo*, to which man belongs, emerged less than a million years ago, while the species *Homo sapiens* has existed for only a fraction of that period. In other forms of life species may differentiate more quickly still.

The changes leading to the creation of new forms of life are caused by a variety of factors whose relative importance is still controversial. Biologists are generally agreed, however, that one of the main factors involved is the influence of the environment. A stable environment tends to produce stable forms of life, while a rapidly changing environment initiates episodes of explosive evolution when many new genera and species are produced.

Now although in general the environment is constantly changing, it seems that in a more restricted sense this is not necessarily the case. In certain circumstances an environment may become locally stable for exceptionally long periods of time. When this occurs its occupants find that they are very little exposed to the necessity for adaptive change; their form and behaviour remain roughly the same until some new factor, such as an alteration in the temperature or the advent of a new predator, disturbs the balance and reinvokes the laws of natural selection. These fortunate creatures, who have found for the time being a calm evolutionary backwater, may not change materially for many millions of years; thus if they survive to our own day they become living fossils.

The existence of several kinds of living fossils has been recognized ever since the 'theory' of evolution became accepted as an established fact. Recently, however, one particular example has specially captured the public imagination and aroused interest in the whole group. This is the coelacanthid fish *Latimeria* which twice in fifteen years has made front page news in newspapers throughout the world. Before I try to show the very great scientific interest of *Latimeria* I will briefly recapitulate the events which led to its discovery.

On December 22nd 1938 a fishing boat under the command of a certain Captain Goosen was trawling about 18 miles south-west of East London, on the southern coast of Africa. It was a fine bright day with little wind and after shooting their lines about 3 miles off shore near the mouth of the Ohalumna river the fishermen began to trawl slowly to the north-east. About 3 miles up the coast they made a broad elliptical sweep out to sea, and then began to hawl up their nets in a depth of just under 40 fathoms.

When the nets had been finally brought aboard and the 'cod-end' slipped, Captain Goosen was delighted to see a pile of fish weighing at least three tons lying on the deck. This was an exceptionally large catch for the area, which was usually reckoned so poor in fish that it was seldom trawled. Sorting the pile took nearly half-an-hour, and it was only when the bottom was reached that one of the crew observed a large and unusual fish about 5 feet long threshing about among its dead and dying companions. Not having seen a similar fish before, he pointed it out to the captain. Goosen and the rest of the crew inspected it with interest, noting the unusual presence of a second dorsal fin and admiring especially the brilliant steel-blue scales and exceptionally large, dark blue eyes. But they did not dare to approach too close for the fish was extremely active and kept snapping viciously at anyone within reach; it was not until over three hours later that it quietened down and finally expired.

The living coelacanth, *Latimeria*

When the trawler returned to port Captain Goosen handed over the fish to Miss Courtenay-Latimer, the Curator of the East London Museum. Miss Courtenay-Latimer was unable to identify the fish herself, but recognized its possible importance and wrote off at once to South Africa's leading ichthyologist, ·

Professor J. L. B. Smith of Rhodes University College, Grahams-town. But unfortunately when the letter arrived the professor was on holiday at Knysa some four hundred miles away, and owing to the Christmas mail congestion news of the discovery did not reach him for ten days. By this time the fish was distinctly high and Miss Courtenay-Latimer decided to have it mounted and throw the flesh and organs away. The only parts she was able to preserve were the skin, the skull, and some portions of the vertebral column and pectoral girdle.

As soon as Professor Smith saw Miss Courtenay-Latimer's sketch and notes he recognized that a zoological discovery of the first importance had been made. The sketch showed that the fish was a coelacanth – a representative of a family that had previously been thought extinct for over 70 million years.

We can imagine the professor's feelings when he got through on the long distance telephone to East London and found that the putrefied body had been disposed of beyond hope of redemption. But, as he made clear at the time, Miss Courte-nay-Latimer could in no way be blamed for her action; she was unaware of the immense significance of the specimen and had taken the most thorough and efficient notes of its anatomy before throwing it away. Later, when the professor had confirmed his identification, he expressed his appreciation of Miss Courtenay-Latimer's work by naming the fish *Latimeria*.

After an exhaustive study of the remains Professor Smith was able to give the scientific world some indication of the significance and importance of *Latimeria*. For a complete description, however, there was nothing for it but to await with as much patience as possible the capture of another specimen. Professor Smith believed that the East London *Latimeria* was probably a stray, and that the most likely habitat of the fish would be moderately deep water in the Mozambique Channel between the French island of Madagascar and the African mainland. His plans for an expedition to this area fell through, but nothing daunted, he prepared a leaflet in English, French and Portuguese giving a brief account and photograph of the fish, and offering a reward of £100 for each of the first two specimens caught. Thousands of these leaflets were distributed to centres in the western Indian Ocean, and Smith and his wife made frequent journeys along the East African coast to impress personally on local authorities the importance of the search.

Finally, after almost exactly fourteen years of waiting, the Professor's patience was rewarded. On the evening of December 20th 1952, a native named Ahmed Hussein was peacefully fishing off the island of Anjouan in the Comoro Archipelago when suddenly his line and fish-baited hook were nearly jerked from his hand. After a hard struggle he managed to pull up a hundred-pound fish of a kind he had never previously seen, and as even after being landed it showed the most aggressive spirit he hit it several times over the head with a piece of wood. This was of course the obvious thing to do, and Ahmed Hussein, who was unaware of the search for the coelacanth, could not have realized that he had thereby irremediably damaged the brain of one of the most valuable prizes ever brought up from the sea. In fact it was only by the purest chance that this second coelacanth – for such it proved to be – was made available for scientific study at all. Hussein carried it off to market where it was about to be cut up for food when another native recognized it as the double of the fish depicted in Professor Smith's leaflet. The carcase was then carried across the island to Captain E. E. Hunt, the skipper of a trading schooner, who with great presence of mind promptly salted it and wired for Professor Smith. Dr Malan, who was at that time Prime Minister of South Africa, placed a special aeroplane at the professor's disposal and he arrived just in time to ensure the proper preservation of the fish with copious injections of formalin. 'When I got to the island', he told reporters afterwards, 'and knelt down to look at the coelacanth lying on its bed of cotton wool, I am not ashamed to say that I wept.' Such is the enthusiasm of the scientist who comes to the end of a long and laborious quest.

The brain of the new specimen, as mentioned above, had been almost completely destroyed, and the body had been severely lacerated by Captain Hunt's natives when they incised it for salting. Nevertheless the soft parts were otherwise well preserved, and Professor Smith estimated that the full examination of the various organs would provide material for at least two years' research. More important still, the home of the coelacanth had been found, and the professor predicted that further specimens would in future be caught with comparative ease. This view proved to be fully justified, for in the following September a third specimen was landed completely intact and taken for examination to the Madagascar Institute of Scientific Research at Antananarivo. By the middle of 1954 the enterprise of the French authorities had led to the capture of three more specimens, while later the same year Professor J. H. Millot of the Musée d'Histoire Naturelle in Paris published the first of four detailed monographs on the subject. Thus in less than sixteen years the structure of this extraordinary living fossil, whose existence had previously never even been suspected, had come within the range of general scientific knowledge.

To some people the expenditure of all this energy and emotion over a 'mere fish' may seem just a trifle ridiculous. But quite apart from its great antiquity and its intrinsic interest, *Latimeria* has several other claims on our attention. Not the least of these is the part played by the group to which it belongs in the evolution of all the land vertebrates, and its close proximity to the ancestry of man himself.

The story begins no less than 300 million years ago in the Devonian Period of geological time. In those distant days animal life was almost entirely confined to the water. Fishes were the dominant creatures, and for this reason the period is sometimes called the Age of Fishes. On the land there was vegetation along the shores of the rivers, lakes and seas, and this formed the home of many kinds of small insects and spiders which had evolved from sea-dwelling forbears at an earlier stage in the Earth's history; but as yet there were no land vertebrates of any kind.

Among the fishes of the Devonian seas and rivers one comparatively small and undiversified group is of particular interest to our present story; this is known to naturalists as the Crossopterygii or 'fringe fins'. Although less numerous and apparently less successful in an aquatic environment than many other groups of fish, the crossopterygians possessed several structural peculiarities which were to be of immense importance in the future history of life. Here it will suffice to mention only two of these. The first is that, in addition to the normal gills of fish, the crossopterygians also had a pair of rudimentary lungs, which enabled them to take their oxygen directly from the air. The second is that they had the fins on the underside of their bodies arranged in two pairs, one fore and one aft, and that these fins were reinforced inside with bone in a way that was reminiscent of the limbs of four-footed land animals.

Scientists are now convinced that it was from creatures of this kind that the first land vertebrates evolved. They believe that during the course of the Devonian Period fishes with lungs and paired fins were gradually learning to leave the water and advancing up the beaches into a new environment. By infinitely slow stages they became more and more successfully adapted to life out of the water. First they evolved into those strange betwixt-and-between creatures the amphibians, which spent a great deal of their time on land but had to return to the water to breed. Then, from the ranks of the amphibians came the reptiles, and finally, from the ranks of the reptiles, came the birds and mammals.

But what, we may ask, has all this to do with our living fossil, *Latimeria*? The point is that *Latimeria* belongs, as mentioned earlier, to an ancient group of fish known as the coelacanths. And the coleacanths constitute one of the main divisions of these very crossopterygian fish we have just been discussing. Thus *Latimeria* can trace its ancestry to the great natural group in which all the land vertebrates, including of course mankind, found their origin.

It is important to realize, however, that this does not mean that *Latimeria* itself is in the main line of human descent. In fact the coelacanth group to which it belongs had already in the Devonian Period diverged too far from the rest of the crossopterygians to be ancestral to man. Scientists now believe that the direct ancestors of the land vertebrates are to be found in another branch of the crossopterygian stock known as the Rhipidistia. Nevertheless *Latimeria* is undoubtedly our cousin, a poor and unenterprising relation who was content to drop away from the main stream of progress and stagnate for 300 million years in an evolutionary backwater.

Owing to the bad state of preservation of the two examples of *Latimeria* examined by Professor Smith, our most exact knowledge of the fish's anatomy comes from the researches of Professor Millot. The professor's monographs on the subject are written mainly for the specialist, but in June 1953 he published in *The Times* an admirable summary of those particular aspects of his discoveries which he thought would be interesting to laymen. These chiefly concerned the animal's fins and heart, which, were of a type which scientists had not previously seen. The fins were of quite exceptional interest. Like the fins of other crossopterygians they contained a complicated internal bony structure anticipating the evolution of vertebrate limbs. But perhaps the most extraordinary thing about them was that their orientation varied by as much as 180 degrees between one fish and another, and even on occasion between the two different sides of the same fish. Put less technically this means that the front edge of, say, the left forward fin, might correspond anatomically with the rear edge of the right forward fin, and that these variations would occur in the same or different specimens without any discernible reason. It is rather as if human beings were not always born with two forward pointing feet, but sometimes with two backward pointing feet, or even with one pointing forward and the other back. This extraordinary flexibility of the coelacanth limb is regarded by Professor Millot as important evidence of the part played by the crossopterygians in the evolution of land life.

Again, the structure of the heart of *Latimeria* was of the greatest interest to students of evolution. The vertebrate heart consists essentially of a simple vascular tube, constricted into four compartments known respectively as the bulbus cordis, the ventricle, the atrium and the sinus venosus. In its most primitive form this tube was probably stretched out in a comparatively straight line, but as evolution progressed it twisted itself gradually into the form of a compact S. This process finally went so far that in an advanced structure like the human heart the atrium and sinus are actually in front of the ventricle. Now the heart of *Latimeria* is so primitive that the S is only beginning to form, and the greater part of the atrium is still behind the ventricle. This makes it the most primitive vertebrate heart yet known to science and provides further confirmation of the way evolution has worked.

I have included these two slightly technical points to show that living fossils are not only a source of great romantic interest, but can furnish clues to the many mysteries that science is constantly attempting to solve. These considerations are especially vital with a living fossil such as *Latimeria* because it is so near to the history of our own race. As Professor Millot wrote in *The Times* (June 3rd 1953): 'The exceptional interest of these fish still depends on the fact that they are incomparable witnesses of a remotely distant era of the living world, stabilized at a particularly important stage in the origin of the higher animals. They should not be considered as belonging to our own line of ancestors; but they are directly related to those ancestors, which they will enable us to know better.'

One last question remains. How is it that this twentieth century coelacanth managed to escape detection for so many years, and was therefore not made available for scientific study until 1938? Several theories have been put forward to explain this odd fact, but none can yet be finally accepted as correct. What seems most likely is that *Latimeria* lives in a very restricted geographical area, and at a depth well below that normally fished with nets. The capture of the East London specimen by a trawler can therefore, it seems, only be regarded as a fortunate accident; as Professor Smith surmised at the time, it was almost certainly a stray, and there was little chance of another coelacanth being caught in similar circumstances. On the other hand, several authorities do not agree with the theory that *Latimeria* is a deep sea fish, and the capture of the second specimen in about 10 fathoms of water lends some support to their view. If they are correct, it is possible that the coelacanths dwell at a moderate depth, but among rocks that would impede the passage of a trawl.

Such speculations are interesting, but for the true facts we shall have to wait until the natural history of the living *Latimeria* is much better known.

CHAPTER TWELVE

A Worm that Wouldn't Turn

La zoologie et la paléontologie sont deux sciences sœurs, qui poursuivant un même idéal, remontent vers l'origine des êtres pour en mieux scruter l'avenir. Elles emploient ordinairement des méthodes différentes, l'une s'adressant à la faune actuelle, l'autre aux restes fossiles des animaux d'autrefois; mais lorsques ces ancêtres ont survécu jusqu'a nous, les deux méthodes sont bien près de se confondre, car alors c'est *directement* que le zoologiste fait l'étude des êtres du passé, et comme le paléontologiste il peut dire: 'Vieux habitants de la terre, apprenez-nous d'où vous êtes venus.'

E. L. Bouvier: *Monographie des Onychophores* (1905)

I do not want to be a fly,
I want to be a worm!
Charlotte P. S. Gilman:
A Conservative

IN the year 1826 a new animal entered the realms of classified zoology. It came from the forested slopes of St. Vincent, an island in the Windward group of the West Indies and, like so many interesting discoveries, it was first described by a parson-naturalist, the Reverend Lansdown Guilding. In the second volume of the *Zoological Journal*, in the issue dated January 1826, we find an article by Guilding headed *An Account of a New Genus of Mollusca*. Although impressively reproduced in Latin, it occupied only just over a page of print, and the casual reader might possibly have been somewhat disappointed to find that it dealt only with an unusual species of slug, 'quae pedibus multis lateralibus distinguitur'. Accompanying the text was a coloured picture of the creature, which looked superficially like a snail without a shell. It measured three inches long, and its body was about the thickness of a pencil. It had 33 pairs of unjointed legs while its head was adorned with two horn-like antennae.

Guilding gave his slug-like animal the name of *Peripatus*, or 'the wandering one,' from the Greek word which was once also used to describe the famous walk in the Lyceum where Aristotle used to stroll while teaching his pupils. The name has stuck to the creature ever since, but Guilding's classification is now known to have been mistaken. Far from being a slug, or even one of the centipedes or millepedes, *Peripatus* is now regarded as a unique member of a special division of the animal kingdom. It is, in fact, a living link between the worms and the insects and is also now generally recognised as the oldest living fossil in the world.

Before digging into the geological past in search of the ancestry of *Peripatus* let us first make a closer inspection of the

Peripatus, the oldest 'living fossil' in the world

living animal. The natural group of which it is the only living genus is known as the Onychophora, or 'claw bearers', the name being derived from the fact that *Peripatus* (pronounced Pe-rip'-ă-tus, by the way, not Peri-pāt'-us, as it is often inaccurately called) has curved claws on the tips of its feet. Since the days of Guilding the genus has been divided into about eighty different species, varying considerably in colour, size and other particulars. The average length is about two to three inches, but some species are smaller than this and a large specimen may measure four inches long. The number of legs varies from fourteen to forty-three pairs, and the colour from dark green or nearly black to bluish grey, brown, or reddish orange. One cave-dwelling species, like the majority of cave animals, has lost its colour altogether.

To anyone unfamiliar with the animal *Peripatus* would probably be regarded either as a caterpillar or a centipede. Thus the famous naturalist Thomas Belt is almost certainly talking of *Peripatus* when he writes in *The Naturalist in Nicaragua* (1874):

In clearing away the fallen logs and brushwoods, many beetles, scorpions, and centipedes were brought to light. Amongst the last was a curious species belonging to the sucking division of the

Myriapods . . . which had a singular method of securing its prey. It is about three inches long, and sluggish in its movements; but from its tubular mouth it is able to discharge a viscid fluid to the distance of about three inches, which stiffens on exposure to the air to the consistency of a spider's web, but stronger. With this it can envelope and capture its prey, just as a fowler throws his net over a bird. The order of *Myriapoda* is placed by systematists at the bottom of the class of insects; the sucking Myriapods are amongst the lowest forms of the order, and it is singular to find one of these lowly organized species furnished with an apparatus of such utility, and the numberless higher forms without any trace of it.

This description fits in very well with many details of *Peripatus* that have since become better known. Like centipedes it lives under logs and stones and piles of damp leaves, and has been reported many times from Central and South America as well as from the hot, humid forests of the Old World south of the Tropic of Cancer. Its capacity to eject a viscous fluid is also well known. Dr Lorus, writing in *Natural History* in April 1954, tells how if *Peripatus* is pressed unexpectedly on the back it raises its head slightly and squirts a gluey substance from two nozzles situated beside the mouth. This hardens as rapidly in the air as nail varnish and does much to immobilize any small creature with which it may come into contact. But Belt seems to have been wrong in believing that this device was used as an offensive weapon. Although *Peripatus* is a carnivore it has never been observed to eat anything caught in this way, even when the trapped animal forms part of its normal diet. The ejaculations are therefore now regarded as automatic responses of a purely defensive kind.

Researches on the feeding habits of *Peripatus* show that it has a most interesting if somewhat repellent method of dealing with its prey. Having sighted a succulent millipede or large termite it extends a lip-like structure which it normally keeps puckered up to hide the mouth, and fixes itself by suction to its intended victim. The skin of the animal is then sliced open by two double bladed jaws placed side by side in the mouth. When an incision has been made, *Peripatus* exudes a strong saliva into the wound which liquefies the flesh so that it can be sucked back with the saliva into the mouth. The whole meal can be extracted in this way through the tiniest of holes, leaving behind only the hollow shell of the unfortunate victim's body.

However, *Peripatus* is not itself immune from certain equally unusual hazards. One of these is that it is quite incapable of sustaining life without a certain degree of humidity. If removed even for a short period from its damp habitat it dries up and dies. This is due to its particularly primitive respiratory system, for *Peripatus* breathes through a number of simple tubes known as trachea which connect the skin with the inner tissues and are widely scattered over the whole surface of the body. Unfortunately there is no mechanism for closing these, and thus if the surrounding atmosphere becomes dry the animal suffers a rapid loss of body moisture. Dr S. M. Manton, who has written a number of standard monographs on *Peripatus*, reports that in an ordinary room as much as a third of the body weight can be lost in four hours. This is roughly twice as much as would be lost by a smooth-skinned caterpillar of equivalent size.

The love life of *Peripatus* has many interesting features. To begin with, the males are normally smaller than the females and have fewer pairs of legs, while the genus resembles the higher animals in that the young are brought forth alive without any intermediate stage in an external egg. There is a definite mating season, but the mating process itself is unconventional and entirely untinged by romance. The male *Peripatus* simply deposits sacs containing sperm cells all over the body of his mate. These sacs are known as spermatophores, and they attract to their immediate region a number of white blood cells from the interior of the animal's body. The blood cells dissolve the skin separating them from the spermatophores, and at the same time a bladder-like vacuole develops just below the point of contact. The sperm cells then emerge from the spermatophore and take up their new residence in the vacuole. From there, under their own power, they infiltrate into the blood stream and eventually arrive at the ovary. Here, if the female is only just sexually mature, the sperms do not immediately fertilize the eggs, but produce chemical substances that are used by the eggs as food. Eventually the eggs burst from the ovary and are then ready for fertilization; but a second supply of male sperms must be made available before this can occur. Finally, there is an additional waiting period of nearly a year before the young are fully formed and can be born. Any surplus sperms resulting

from the second act of coition are used to feed the next generation of eggs. Thus the female *Peripatus* carries two sets of eggs in
her body, one ripening into fully formed young, the other feeding
on sperm remnants preparatory to emerging from the ovary.

But reproduction is only one of the many aspects of *Peripatus*
that has been the subject of detailed study. In Bouvier's monograph, published in 1907, the bibliography cites no less than
210 references to this extraordinary little animal, while in
recent years the flood of papers on the genus has not diminished
but increased. To quote only one example, in 1945 Dr Manton
devoted a 41 page treatise to its method of locomotion alone.
Here we are fascinated to read that *Peripatus*, like the less
advanced patterns of motor car, has three gears of which 'top'
'can only be used after sufficient speed has been acquired by the
use of the "bottom" and "middle gear" gaits'. Cinematograph
films and a study of *Peripatus* tracks on smoked paper have
enabled scientists to work out the mechanics of these 'gears'
in the minutest detail. And there is now hardly a feature of the
natural history of *Peripatus* that has not been made the subject
of equally intensive research.

Even the aesthetic aspects of this unusual worm-insect have
not been entirely neglected. To many people *Peripatus* probably
represents just another 'creepy-crawly', to be classified with
millipedes, earthworms, woodlice, spiders and other vaguely
repellent creatures whose traditional role is to cause consternation among young ladies at picnic parties. But to the enthusiast
Peripatus can present quite a different picture. Let me quote,
for example, the words of Professor Adam Sedgwick, the
famous nineteenth century English geologist. 'Peripatus', he
writes, 'though a lowly organised animal, and of remarkable
sluggishness, with but slight development of the higher organs
of sense, with eyes the only function of which is to enable it to
avoid the light – though related to those animals most repulsive
to the aesthetic sense of man, animals which crawl upon their
bellies and spit at, or poison, their prey – is yet, strange to say,
an animal of striking beauty. The exquisite sensitiveness and
constantly changing form of the antennae, the well-rounded
plump body, the eyes set like diamonds on the side of the head,
the delicate feet, and, above all, the rich colouring and velvety
texture of the skin, all combine to give these animals an aspect

of quite exceptional beauty. Of all the species which I have seen alive, the most beautiful are the dark green individuals of *Capensis*, and the species which I have called *Balfouri*. These animals, so far as skin is concerned, are not to be surpassed in the animal kingdom'.

So much, then, for the living animal; but why is it being considered here in a section devoted to living fossils? To answer this question we must go back to the year 1911, when on September 4th the American palaeontologist Charles Doolittle Walcott published a paper called *Middle Cambrian Annelids* under the auspices of the Smithsonian Institution in Washington. The term 'annelid' refers to the natural class Annelida, which contains a great variety of segmented worms, some living today and others well known from fossil imprints and trackways in the rocks of the geological past. The term Middle Cambrian indicates that Walcott was talking about remains of annelids found in rocks of the Middle Cambrian period – that is to say, rocks that are between 450 million and 500 million years old.

Among the annelid worms that Walcott described was one which he regarded as belonging to an entirely new family and genus. It had been found in a band of dark siliceous shale about 4 feet thick, which formed part of a rock system known to geologists as the Stephen formation. The particular outcrop which produced the specimen lay on the slope of a ridge about 3,800 feet above the town of Field on the British Columbia section of the Canadian Pacific Railway. Walcott named his specimen *Aysheaia pedunculata* after the mountain peak of Ayshea in British Columbia, and a composite Latin word of which the best translation in this context is probably 'stalk-footed'.

Now the discovery of a new genus of annelids was not so very surprising; in fact, this very monograph of Walcott's is full of families, genera and species that were being described for the first time. But it was not long before someone spotted that *Aysheaia* was in all probability not an annelid at all, but a member of the Onychophora, the order that also included the living *Peripatus*. The discovery of several new species confirmed this view, and in 1930 the whole genus was restudied by another American scientist, Dr George E. Hutchinson, of the Osborn Zoological Laboratory of Yale University. As a result of these and other researches it has now been established not only that *Peripatus* had its origin in this group of animals which lived at such a remote period in the past, but also that it has persisted with relatively little change from that day to this.

The duration of geological time in terms of figures is almost as difficult to grasp as the immensity of astronomical space; thus to enable us to appreciate the great antiquity of the *Peripatus* line of descent an illustration may perhaps be of use. Let us imagine for a moment that we are walking back into the past, and that each of our strides is equivalent to a thousand years. The first stride would take us to the Norman Conquest, the second to the time of Julius Caesar, the tenth to the end of the Old Stone Age. During the next 500 strides we should pass through the whole evolutionary history of man, but even so (if we assume that each of our strides is about a yard in length) we should still be only just over quarter of a mile from our starting point. A distance of 40 miles would bring us to the end of the Age of Dinosaurs and a further 120 miles to a time when fishes were the dominant creatures on the Earth. But to reach the time of *Aysheaia*, the forerunner of *Peripatus*, we should have to walk a total distance of no less than 284 miles.

Of course it should not be assumed that *Aysheaia* and *Peripatus* are identical. During the Cambrian Period, which is the earliest named period of geological time, there was no land life of any kind. *Aysheaia* was therefore an aquatic animal, an inhabitant of the warm shallow seas that in Cambrian times were encroaching on much of the land. The segments of the body were less numerous than in *Peripatus* and there were fewer pairs of legs. Other differences were apparent in the arrangement of the antennae, the number of claws on each leg, and the position of the mouth. But even when these points are considered, *Peripatus* shows extraordinarily little variation from the primitive onychophore stock. The only important modifications that have taken place are those associated with the change over from a marine to a terrestial way of life. For instance the mouth has moved from the front of the body to the underside, a far more suitable position for a land-dwelling animal of this kind. And the development of trachea for breathing air, which are absent in *Aysheaia*, is another obvious adaptation to life out of the water.

Equipped with this information concerning the onychophores

and their long geological history, we must come back next to the statement made earlier in this chapter that *Peripatus* is in all probability a living link between two great natural divisions of the animal kingdom – the worms and the insects. Although there are many obvious differences between these two groups there are also several significant likenesses. For example, the nervous system in each case is constructed on a remarkably similar plan, while even in such external features as the segmentation of a worm's body and a beetle's abdomen there are enough resemblances to suggest a common origin. As a result of such likenesses students of evolution are now reasonably sure that both worms and insects are descended from a single ancestral stock.

Now what is particularly interesting is that the living *Peripatus* seems to combine in its own person features that are normally associated either with worms or with insects, but never with both. To take only a few random examples, its eyes, excretory system and surface musculature resemble those found in the living segmented worms, while its circulatory system and breathing mechanism resemble those found in insects. In external features also there is the same mixture of characters. Thus the general appearance of *Peripatus* is reminiscent of that of a worm, but it nevertheless has legs equipped with insect-like claws.

What, then, is the evolutionary picture that results from a study of *Peripatus* and the two groups whose characters it shares? It seems that sometime between 1,000 million and 500 million years ago a race of primitive marine invertebrates was beginning a twofold differentiation. One line of descent led to the insects and the related divisions of the phylum Arthropoda, while the other led to the annelid worms. At the same time a number of conservative members of the same great group declined the choice of following either of these alternatives and remained stabilized at the particular level of evolution they had then attained. Millennium followed millennium and life increased in variety and complexity; but the only change made by this small and unenterprising group was to transfer their home from the sea to the land. *Aysheaia* represents one of the earliest stages in this long and uneventful history. We can see the most recent in the various species of *Peripatus* – descendents of a line that has persisted almost unchanged for over half of the whole history of life.

CHAPTER THIRTEEN

Relics of the Primeval Forest

For it had bene an auncient tree,
Sacred with many a mysteree. . . .
SPENSER: *The Shepheardes Calendar* (*Februarie*)

And here were forests ancient as the hills,
Enfolding sunny spots of greenery.
COLERIDGE: *Kubla Khan*

. . . the trees
That whisper round a temple become soon
Dear as the temple's self. KEATS: *Endymion*

ONE of the few ways in which a writer may occasionally indulge himself is to be able to choose the time and place of his work. On this summer afternoon I am sitting in a deck chair on a lawn outside the Fellows Restaurant at the London Zoo contemplating the subject of my next chapter. And I do not use the word contemplating in a purely metaphorical sense, for to my right, just in front of an enclosure where a pair of bactrian camels are regarding the passing crowds with a supercilious stare, stand four of the oldest living fossils in the world. Strangely enough, however, no one takes much notice of them. It seems that their main purpose in life is a purely practical one, namely to provide support for children who clamber on the railings of the Fellows' Lawn in order to get a better view of the Chimpanzees' Tea Party. And yet these four relics of the past are as remarkable in their own way as would be four living dinosaurs in the same surroundings. They are the descendants of a line which flourished in the distant past of the Earth when the reptiles themselves were young, when the first flying birds had not yet evolved, and when our own ancestors were still tiny shrew-like creatures scurrying timidly through the undergrowth of the primeval forests. Why, then, do they attract so little attention? Perhaps it is because they are not themselves mammals or birds, or even reptiles, but simply trees.

Let us walk over and examine these living botanical fossils a

little more closely. The label on each of them – for all belong to
the same species – declares that they were scientifically classified
by Linnaeus, the great Swedish botanist, as *Ginkgo biloba*, or
'the twin-lobed ginkgo'. For those who dislike scientific ter-
minology, even when it is as attractive as this, there is also

A grove of maidenhair trees, *Ginkgo biloba*

printed the alternative English name of Maidenhair Tree. The
reason for both these names is made apparent by a glance at
the leaves. Each leaf is divided into two clearly defined segments or 'lobes', while if we are fanciful and prepared to stretch
a point or two, we can see that the veins of each segment,
fanning out from a central point, give it the appearance of a
hank of girl's hair.

If we now stand back a little so as to get the whole of the tree
within our range of vision, we shall see the straight trunk, with
its covering of rough, grey bark, rising upward to a height of
between 20 and 30 feet. The branches are arranged in rather
an odd way. Instead of forking outwards and upwards from the
trunk like the branches of more familiar trees, most of them
stick out from it almost at right angles, like long, slender pegs.
On each tree there are usually two or three branches which are
much longer than the rest. These occur at irregular intervals up
the trunk for no apparent reason, and give the tree a strangely
unsymmetrical appearance. Sometimes by chance two of

these long branches may grow out from the trunk at nearly the same height, but on opposite sides of it. When this happens (as in a famous specimen at Kew Gardens) the tree bears a striking resemblance to the mast of a sailing ship supporting a pair of yard-arms.

Ginkgo belongs to the natural botanical group of the Gymnospermae or 'naked seeded' plants; this is one of the two great divisions of living seed-bearers, the other being the Angiospermae, or 'seed-vesseled' plants. The angiosperms include an enormous number of types ranging from the great forest trees to the smallest flowers and herbs, and even the simple duckweed of the village pond. By comparison the gymnosperms are less varied and more primitive. They are nevertheless exceedingly familiar to us, being the group which contains such common conifers as pines, cedars, larches, firs, yews and so on, as well as the palm-like cycads of the tropics, the redwoods of the western United States, and several groups of extinct plants that are well known from their fossil remains.

Ginkgo, unlike most gymnosperms, is a deciduous tree, and in autumn its leaves turn a particularly beautiful shade of golden brown before falling. One of the most interesting features of the genus is that the trees can be individually sexed, male reproductive organs being borne on one tree and female on another. The male organs consist of loose catkins, each normally having a pair of pollen sacs; the female organs are larger and longer, with two ovules which develop into fleshy yellow seeds about the size of cherries. Inside the fleshy covering the embryo and the food that has been stored for it by its parent are protected by a hard shell. The fruit itself at the best of times is somewhat tasteless, and if over-ripe can be nauseating; but the embryo and food inside the hard shell have a pleasing and characteristic flavour which causes them to be regarded as a delicacy in China and Japan, where ginkgos are most common.

At one time *Ginkgo* used to be classified with the conifers. Despite obvious differences in the form of the leaves and the structure of the flowers, it was regarded as a close relation of the yew. But then an interesting discovery was made which caused this view to be fundamentally changed. At the end of the last century the Japanese botanist Hirase was working on

Ginkgo when he discovered an unusual feature connected with the male reproductive cells. In all angiosperms and conifers the male sperm, which is extremely small, cannot move of its own volition but is carried to the female cell by means of a slender tube, known as the pollen-tube. But in *Ginkgo*, Hirase discovered, the male cells are relatively huge, and lash their own way to the female cell by means of tiny hairs known as cilia. Without going into further technicalities, this fact was sufficient to remove *Ginkgo* finally from the conifer group and place it in a new class, the Ginkgoales, of which it is the only living representative.

Although *Ginkgo* is now widespread in cultivation its natural habitat is limited to remote areas in China. Even there, according to some authorities, it has only returned to a secondary wild state after a previous period of cultivation. However this may be, it has certainly been cultivated for many centuries in China and Japan. In these countries where it is, so as to speak, on its home ground, *Ginkgo* grows very much larger than it does in its new artificial environments in Europe and the United States. Some large specimens may attain a height of a hundred feet or more, and are among the most magnificent of oriental trees. The trunks of old specimens grow pendulous air-roots like stalactites, and the fancied resemblance of these to the human female breast has given the tree great symbolic significance among Chinese and Japanese women. According to Sir Albert Seward, one of Britain's most eminent palaeobotanists, a giant ginkgo at Sendai, in northern Japan, has been worshipped for over a thousand years by women suffering from lack of milk or any sickness of the breasts.

Cultivated ginkgos in China and Japan are almost invariably found in the neighbourhood of temples, or in areas where temples once stood. This suggests that *Ginkgo* was formerly a sacred tree, and even today the Japanese peasants ascribe to it several peculiar virtues. For example, it is held to be a sure protection against fire, the legend stating that when scorched by flames it exudes so much moisture that the fire is immediately extinguished. This is not such an extravagant conception as one might think, for according to a friend of Seward's ginkgos are exceptionally resistent to fire and will survive almost unhurt when other trees are destroyed. As I tried to show in Part I of this book, it is not so very unusual for superstition and natural history to combine in this way to form a half-truth.

In the Middle Ages the Chinese used to call the ginkgo the 'duck's foot tree', and this is certainly a more apt way of describing its leaves than by any comparison with maidens' hair. The name ginkgo itself seems to have been coined at the end of the seventeenth century by the German naturalist,

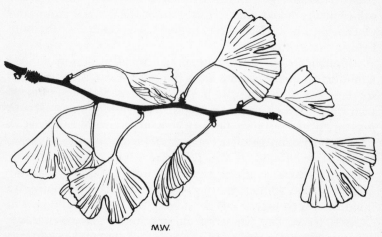

M.W.

The leaves of *Ginkgo biloba*, showing their fanciful resemblance to a 'maiden's hair'

physician and traveller, Engelberg Kaempfer. In 1682 Dr Kaempfer had gone as private secretary on a Swedish ambassadorial mission to Persia. Instead of returning home at the end of the mission he took a job with the Dutch East India Company and ended up in 1690 as physician to the Dutch Embassy in Nagasaki. No sooner had he arrived there than he was struck by the magnificent groves of ginkgos that were everywhere to be seen. In 1712 he published a description of the tree, with an excellent illustration of its leaves and fruit, in his book *Amoenitatum exoticarum*. Even for those who, like myself, have little Latin and less Greek, the opening of his description is impressive by its sonority alone. After giving the name *Ginkgo* in Chinese and Roman lettering, the alternative, *Ginau* and the popular name, *Itsjo*, he proceeds: 'Arbor nucifera folio Andiantino. Liberali Juglandis vastitate exsurgit; *Caudice* dotata longo, recto, crasso, ramoso; cortice cinereo, ob vetustatem scabro & lacunoso. . . .' And so on in the same vein.

A few years later Kaempfer gave an abbreviated account of *Ginkgo* in his *History of Japan*, which was translated into English in 1727. He writes: 'Another sort of Nuts, call'd *Ginan* as big as large *Pistaches* grow very plentifully almost everywhere in *Japan* on a fine tall tree, the leaves of which are not unlike the large leaves of an *Adianthum*. The Japanese call it *Itsionoki*. The Nuts afford plenty of Oyl, which is much commended for several uses.'

The next chapter in the story of *Ginkgo* is recounted most fully in the fourth volume of a book called *Arboretum et Fruticetum Britannicum* (1838) by the Scottish horticultural writer John Claudius Loudon. Loudon tells how this obscure tree, formerly unknown outside China and Japan, began in the eighteenth century to be cultivated throughout the world by enthusiasts for botanical curiosities. It had reached Europe a few years after its discovery and, although the facts are not definitely known, the oldest specimen is reputed to be that in the Botanical Gardens at Utrecht. According to scientific estimates this was probably planted in the second or third decade of the eighteenth century.

In England ginkgos had definitely made their appearance by 1754. In fact it was a British enthusiast named Gordon who sent the first ginkgo seedling to Linnaeus for an authorative opinion and description. This was in 1771, and in the same year the master described the plant in his book *Mantissa*, retaining *Ginkgo* as the name of the genus, and adding the trivial name of *biloba*. But despite his reputation the scientific name given by Linnaeus was by no means universally accepted among the would-be pundits of nomenclature. In 1796 the famous botanist Sir James Smith proposed the alternative designation of *Salisburia adiantifolia*, branding the name *Ginkgo* as 'uncouth and barbarous'. This was doubtless because it was originally derived from a Chinese word of uncertain etymology whose only known component was the syllable 'gin' meaning silver. Fortunately, however, Smith's suggested emendation never found favour, and the tree has ever since retained the apt and exotic name conferred upon it by Linnaeus.

After *Ginkgo* had become firmly established in England, British botanists began to send its seeds to their friends and colleagues in different parts of the world. Thus it was planted in Rouen in 1776, in Paris in 1780, in Schönbrunn in 1781, and finally, in 1784, it reached North America, where it was to become one of the favourite ornamental trees of the United States. The story of its arrival in Paris is particularly entertaining and I cannot do better than tell it in the words of John Loudon who has placed it on permanent record.

'In 1780', he writes, 'a Parisian amateur, named Pétigny, made a voyage to London, in order to see the principal gardens; and among the number of those he visited was that of a commercial gardener, who possessed five young plants of *Ginkgo biloba*, which was still rare in England, and which the gardener pretended that he then alone possessed. These five plants were raised from nuts that he had received from Japan; and he set a high price on them. However, after an abundant *déjeûné*, and plenty of wine, he sold to M. Pétigny these young trees of *Ginkgo*, all growing in the same pot, for 25 guineas, which the Parisian amateur paid immediately, and lost no time in taking away his valuable acquisition. Next morning, the effects of the wine being dissipated, the English gardener sought out his customer, and offered him 25 guineas for one plant of the five he had sold the day before. This, however, was refused by M. Pétigny, who carried the plants to France; and, as each of the five had cost him about 120 francs, or 40 crowns (*quarante écus*), this was the origin of the name applied to this tree in France, of *arbre aux quarante écus*; and not because it was originally sold for 120 francs a plant. Almost all the ginkgo trees in France have been propagated from these five, imported from England by M. Pétigny.'

Despite the fact that *Ginkgo* has now spread to every part of Europe, and has even been persuaded to grow in the inhospitable climate of Scotland, it is in the United States that it has enjoyed its most spectacular success. Since the first ginko was planted there on an estate in Philadelphia in 1784 the tree has spread over the whole country. Town planning authorities have taken it up, and in some American cities avenues of ginkgos are now as common as avenues of chestnuts or planes in England. One interesting fact is that all the American ginkgos seem to have been imported from Europe, none directly across the Pacific from China or Japan.

But this amazing spread of a single tree by human agency across nearly the whole of the northern hemisphere in less than two hundred years is not the only remarkable fact we now know about *Ginkgo*. In the middle of the nineteenth century the palaeobotanists began to take a hand; as their work proceeded it was realized that *Ginkgo biloba* was no ordinary tree, which had aroused the curiosity of botanists simply because of its rarity and unusual structure. It was the last survivor of a genus which in its natural state had once occurred over almost the whole of the land surface of the globe, and whose fossil history ran into many scores of millions of years.

It is now over a hundred years since the first specimens of fossilized leaves of *Ginkgo* were found in the Tertiary rocks of northern Italy. These dated from the Eocene Epoch, which lasted from approximately 70 million to 45 million years ago. Since then numerous other examples have been found from every geological Epoch down to the Holocene, or wholly recent. For instance the leaves of ginkgos have been found in Pliocene strata near Frankfurt-on-Main in Germany, and in the Rhone valley in France where dense forests once ran down to a large gulf which then covered much of the present land of Provence.

Some of the most beautiful Tertiary ginkgo fossils came from the Island of Mull. At the dawn of the Tertiary Period violent volcanic activity broke out in this area and in the neighbouring lands, and masses of white-hot basalt streamed from volcanoes and other fissures in the Earth's crust to form gigantic lava fields. The rocks of Fingal's Cave in the island of Staffa, and the strange conformation of the Giant's Causeway in Northern Ireland, bear witness to this period of crisis and catastrophe in the ancient landscape of the Earth. But between successive outbursts of volcanic activity there were periods of calm. At these times water-borne sediments spread over the lava fields, and the stricken landscape gradually reassumed its mantle of green. In the forests of that time *Ginkgo* was a common tree, and its fossilized leaves are virtually indistinguishable in shape and general structure from the leaves of ginkgos alive today.

But the Eocene is a comparatively late stage in the history of *Ginkgo*. In the preceding Mesozoic Era, the Age of the Dinosaurs, this venerable race of trees flourished in every quarter of the globe. To quote Sir Albert Seward: 'Some of the leaves from the Jurassic rocks near Scarborough bear a striking resemblance in size, shape, and venation to the modern type of foliage and differ only in comparatively minor structural characters.' In this middle period of the Age of the Dinosaurs there were ginkgos not only in China and Japan, but in Australia and New Zealand, in Afghanistan, Turkestan and Siberia, in Sardinia and throughout the continent of Europe, and in North America as far west as Oregon on the Pacific coast. In the still earlier Triassic Period, which ended over 170 million years ago, ginkgos flourished in places as far apart as Greenland, Indo-China, South Africa, Australia and southern Sweden. Although there were certain differences in detail, the lay eye would have found it hard to distinguish these ancient trees from the four specimens at the London Zoo.

Even yet, however, the geological history of *Ginkgo* is not exhausted. Back in the Permian Period, before the mammals or even the dinosaurs existed, we have fossil evidence of certain enigmatical plants, such as *Ginkgophyllum* and *Psygmophyllum*, whose structure is suggestive of an ancestral relationship to the ginkgos. In the still earlier Carboniferous Period, the Age of the Coal Forests, when the first sea creatures had only partially achieved their invasion of the land, there are further ginkgo-like remains. But in both these distant geological Periods we are not on firm scientific ground. It seems likely that plants lived at that time whose affinities with the ginkgos may one day be proved; but further than that we cannot go.

One final question remains. How was it that *Ginkgo*, one of the most successful trees of the primeval forest, with a distribution extending over the larger portion of the globe, was eventually driven into retreat in a remote corner of China, and was only able to re-establish itself with human protection and encouragement? There is no certain answer to this question, but it seems likely that the eclipse of *Ginkgo* in the Tertiary Period was caused by the same great geological and climatic changes which led to the extinction of the Mesozoic reptiles and the rise to power of the comparatively new race of warm-blooded mammals. As the mammals, with their greater activity and bigger brains, succeeded the cold-blooded reptiles, so did the more adaptable angiosperms succeed the flourishing gymnosperms of earlier times. Of course some of the gymnosperms found themselves a secluded evolutionary niche where they could continue to live relatively undisturbed; but others such as *Ginkgo* fell victims to adverse circumstances and were only saved from extinction by the intervention of man.

Here, for once, man has shown his wisdom, for *Ginkgo* has perhaps a greater significance to us even than its interest as a unique botanical specimen. If I may be allowed to quote once more from Sir Albert Seward: '*Ginkgo* is one of a small company of living plants which illustrates continuity and exceptional power of endurance in a changing world. . . . When we regard the earth's surface in terms of the ordinary time-scale it gives us an impression of stability; adopting the time-scale of geologists we are able to measure the duration of earlier periods; as we pass from one age to another we can follow the shifting boundaries of continents and seas. With minds prepared by thoughts derived from a geological retrospect *Ginkgo* becomes much more to us than a mere tree; it speaks to us as an oracle recording in the trembling accents of its fluttering leaves the varying fortunes of its race and wanderings over the world's surface as age succeeded age; it gives us glimpses of the great procession of life and the building of the world in which we live.'

CHAPTER FOURTEEN

The Attic of the Earth

Father Noah and his sons, they invited to the Ark
  A distinguished group of mammals, all placental,
But they snubbed the duck-billed platypus and jumping kangaroo
  In a manner that was very far from gentle.

To the Talgai boy they hinted he was nothing but a moron
  Whom principles eugenic would condemn,
That they'd better let him perish than continue as a menace
  To society, and Japheth, Ham, and Shem.

So he called the big *Diprotodon* and on his back he climbed,
  And he whistled to the friendly dingo, too;
And platypus and wombat and the rest fell in behind,
  As frequently the simple-minded do.

They jumped upon an island that kindly floated by
  And they drifted far to southern seas unknown,
Where these brave Marsupialia in a land we call Australia
  Formed a doughty little kingdom of their own.

Now the scientists pedantic who defend the bridge Atlantic,
  When they hear this tale authentic I'd advise
To apologize quite meekly to these creatures who uniquely
  Controverted an hypothesis so wise.

E. H. FINK: *An Arkaeological Epic*

FROM the beginning of recorded history the human mind has been fascinated with the idea of distant places and strange forms of life. One of the main obsessions of the early travellers was with the existence of a great Southern Continent lying below the horizon of the Indian Ocean. The nature of this continent and its inhabitants was unknown, but it was generally regarded by Aristotle and his followers as being in every way analogous to the continents of the north. Pliny actually reported how a Roman freedman had visited this *Terra Australis* or *Terra Incognita* as it was variously called, and had been hospitably entertained by its inhabitants. But then he disappointed his readers by identifying it with the newly discovered island of Ceylon.

The church was generally opposed to the idea of the Southern Continent. Thus Lactantius Firmianus, known as the 'Christian Cicero', who lived in the third century A.D., deplored the stupidity of those who believed in the existence of lands where men walked upside down, where trees had their branches higher than their roots and rivers flowed up hill. Again, in the eighth century, the Irish priest Virgilius, who had been convinced by reading ancient books that a Southern Continent might exist, was actually condemned as a heretic by Pope Zacharias for holding a view so contrary to the revealed facts of religion. Even that wise and intelligent churchman St. Augustine of Hippo (to whom, ironically enough, several Australian churches are now dedicated) pointed out that there was no scriptural authority for such an absurd belief.

Today, of course, it is known that the Southern Continent as conceived by the Greeks and later thinkers has had no solid existence during the present Era of geological time. (Whether this is true of other Eras in Earth history is a subject we shall return to later.) But the discoveries of the early voyagers in the Pacific and Indian Oceans revealed the existence of several lands no less remarkable. The most important of these were New Zealand, Antarctica, and the great continental island of Australia, whose natural history will form the main subject of the present chapter.

To a naturalist Australia and its neighbouring islands constitute a unique region. With the exception of a few later importations it is inhabitated entirely by animals that have survived from an extremely remote period in the geological past. It is, in fact, a land of living fossils, a vast storehouse of ancient animals, where we can study forms of life that elsewhere have been extinct for many millions of years.

The most spectacular of these survivals are contained in two main natural groups. There are firstly the Marsupialia, or pouched mammals, including the familiar kangaroo and a multitude of lesser known species; and secondly the Monotremata, or egg-laying mammals, represented by the echidna, or spiny anteater, and that extraordinary relic of the past, the duck-billed platypus. The monotremes are entirely confined to the Australian region, and the marsupials are only represented elsewhere by the opossums and a few other small New World forms. It may therefore come as a surprise to those who associate the discovery of Australia with Captain Cook, or at the earliest with the voyages of the Dutch merchants of the Middle Ages, when they learn that marsupials had already been described in the second century A.D. The first mention of them occurs in the writings of Lucian of Samosata, the leading exponent of the revived Greek literature which appeared under the Roman Empire. He mentions reports of animals that 'use their belly like a pouch: it opens and shuts: there is nothing in it, but it is shaggy and hairy, so that their young creep into it when cold'. Lucian himself would not accept such tall stories; but they nevertheless prove that men had come in contact with marsupials more than eighteen centuries ago.

Modern marsupials are descendants of a primitive group of mammals, whose history began towards the end of the Age of the Dinosaurs. The pouch, or marsupium, which contains the teats, is normally situated on the belly of the female, and the young are carried and nourished in it for some time after their birth. The reason for this is that the great majority of marsupials lack the organ known as a placenta which in the higher mammals enables the young to be nourished in the womb. Young marsupials must therefore emerge into the world at an earlier stage than the young of placental mammals, and in consequence need a greater measure of protection for some time after their birth.

The kangaroo is the best known and most spectacular of the marsupials in the Australasian region. There are numerous species ranging from the tiny wallabies of the genus *Dorcopsis*, which are confined to New Guinea and are no larger than rabbits, to the red kangaroo and great grey kangaroo of the Australian plains, which when standing erect on their hind legs are the height of a tall man.

Captain Cook is often credited with being the first European to report the presence of kangaroos in Australia, but already in 1629, well over a century before Cook's first voyage round the world, the Dutch sea captain François Pelsaert had seen them after his ship, the *Batavia*, had been wrecked on the Abrolhos reef. They were sighted again in the same region in 1699 by that famous traveller Captain William Dampier, variously known as 'The Learned and Faithful Dampier', 'The Prince of Voyagers', and 'The Buccaneer'. During his wild and romantic career Dampier made two visits to Australia (or New Holland as it was then called), the first in 1688 in the *Cygnet*, the second in 1699 in the *Roebuck*. On the second visit when, like Pelsaert but less disastrously, he reached the west coast in the neighbourhood of the Abrolhos reef, he wrote in his Journal: 'The Land-Animals that we saw here were only a Sort of Raccoons, different from those of the West Indies, chiefly as to their Legs; for these have very short Fore-Legs; but go jumping upon them as the others do, (and like them are very good Meat).' Despite the obvious slip of the pen which gives the impression that the animals jumped on their fore-legs instead of their hind-legs, there can be little doubt that this description refers to the dama wallaby, *Macropus eugenii*, which still lives in south-western Australia and on the coastal islands.

These preliminary sightings were confirmed by Captain Cook when he voyaged to Australia in the bark *Endeavour* between 1768 and 1771. He tells in his Journal how on Saturday June 23rd 1770, while in the region of Endeavour River, Queensland, he sent three of the crew into the country to shoot pigeons. 'One of the Men', he reports, 'saw an Animal something less than a greyhound; it was of a Mouse Colour, very slender made and swift of Foot.' The following day Cook himself saw one of these strange animals, and on July 14th a small specimen was shot by John Gore, the second officer. Cook writes: 'the head, neck, and Shoulders [were] very Small in proportion to the other parts. It was hair lipt, and the Head and Ears were most like a Hare's of any Animal I know; the Tail was nearly as long as the body, thick next the Rump, and Tapering towards the End; the fore Legs were 8 Inches long, and the Hind 22. Its progression is by Hopping or Jumping 7 or 8 feet at each hop upon its hind Legs only, for in this it makes no use of the Fore, which seem to be only design'd for Scratching in the ground, etc. . . . It bears no sort of resemblance to any European animal I ever saw.' The following month Sir Joseph Banks, the naturalist to the expedition, heard what he believed to be the native name for the animal. This he interpreted as kangooroo or kanguru, and so the word 'kangaroo' entered the catalogues of natural science. It has been retained ever since, despite the fact that no known Australian dialect possesses such a word: as Carl Hartman has recently suggested, perhaps a native cleared his throat at the critical moment and was thus unexpectedly immortalized.

The kangaroo well exemplifies the strangely primitive reproduction methods of the marsupial group. When the young

The kangaroo, most familiar of the Australian marsupials

are born they are tiny, naked creatures about an inch in length. But despite their diminutive size their limbs are sufficiently strong and well developed to enable them to pull themselves through the mothers fur and find their way into the pouch. Here they instinctively fasten themselves to the nipple which at this time is pointed and firm. But once enclosed by the mouth of the young it softens and expands to such an extent that it cannot be removed. The young maintains this enforced contact with the nipple for about four months, during which time milk is pumped into it by involuntary contractions of the muscles of the mother's mammary glands. But as soon as it has grown to sufficient size and maturity to detach itself the young kangaroo begins to pop its head out of the pouch and take an interest in the outside world. Eventually it sallies forth altogether to enjoy its first attempts at active life. During the first weeks of infancy, however, it will always return to its refuge in the pouch whenever it is tired or frightened.

Although this primitive kind of reproduction is typical of the marsupials, the kangaroo itself is a highly specialized animal and its geological history is too short to enable it to rank as a true living fossil. To obtain an idea of what the ancestral marsupials of 70 million years ago were like we must look at some of the smaller and more generalized living forms. Two main divisions of marsupials are recognized, distinguished anatomically by differences in the number of their incisor teeth. The first division, known as the Diprotodonta, consists entirely of vegetarians, and numbers among its representatives not only the living kangaroos, wombats and 'koala bears', but also several extinct forms such as the Pleistocene giant, *Diprotodon*, which was roughly the size of a modern rhinoceros. It is, however, the second division, known as the Polyprotodonta, which is particularly interesting to us from an historical point of view. This is the sub-order which includes the so-called 'native cats' of Australia, the American opossums, and a number of other remarkable carnivorous and omnivorous forms.

Although Australia is the home of most of the modern marsupials it so happens that the forms that bear most resemblance to the ancient fossil species are the American opossums of the family Didelphidae. These were discovered as long ago as 1500, when the explorer Vicente Pinzón brought a female opossum from Brazil to the court of Ferdinand and Isabella of Spain. The king and queen, it is said, were so fascinated by this wonder of nature that they were constrained to explore the interior of

The American opossum

its pouch with their own royal fingers. The publicity given to the opossum by this episode, as well as by the accounts of such sixteenth century writers as Peter Martyr, Angelo Trevigliano, and Richard Eden, soon brought it international fame as a curiosity of the animal world.

Despite its early notoriety and its interest to us as a living fossil the American opossum is not a particularly attractive animal. There are numerous species ranging from the United States to the Argentine, but they are mostly similar in habits. The typical opossum is a small nocturnal and arboreal animal with prominent black eyes and a prehensile tail. Pinzón described its ears as thin and black like a bat's and this is quite correct. The head and muzzle are pointed and the braincase exceptionally small, which makes the opossum an exasperatingly stupid animal, at least in captivity. The smell is said to be unalluring, but I personally do not find it worse than that of many other small mammals; it is certainly less offensive than that of the underground railway in the rush hour. Despite its limited intelligence, the opossum has a certain instinctive craft; for instance its habit of feigning death, or 'playing possum', when frightened is well known.

But what is most interesting to us in the present context is that the living opossum is an almost exact replica of its ancestors of over 70 million years ago. Admittedly the fossil forms tend to be somewhat smaller and to show certain variations in detail, but a comparison of the teeth and bones shows that the similarities are far more significant than the differences. Moreover the fossil remains of the ancient opossums show that they were very generalized creatures; in other words, they had not yet committed themselves to exaggerated specializations which would lead them along a definite evolutionary path. In fact, it seems likely that ancient opossum-like animals were the ancestors of the whole marsupial group. One line, which led to the modern opossums, remained little changed, but others branched out, each concentrating on a different set of special adaptations. And it is the end-products of these diverging lines, all stemming from the original opossum-like stock, that constitute the varied population of marsupials that we know today.

Returning from the American opossum to the Australasian marsupials, we find that here too there are forms reminiscent of the generalized ancestors of the whole group. The most direct descendants of the original stock are probably the carnivorous dasyures, or 'native cats'. In fact they are often referred to, incorrectly, as opossums, despite the fact that they are not particularly close relations of the American family. Other fairly primitive Australasian marsupials include a number of mouse-like insectivorous forms, and that extraordinary creature, the Tasmanian devil, *Sarcophilus harrisii*, which is a small but powerful carnivore, of sinister aspect and highly predacious habits.

In spite of the different adaptations acquired by many marsupials during the past 70 million years, the group as a whole is so ancient and primitive that we can fairly regard it as consisting entirely of living fossils. This is true also of the other group of Australasian animals we must now briefly mention, the monotremes, or egg-laying mammals. Although the fossil history of the two living members of this group is virtually unknown, they possess such an extraordinary mixture of reptilian and mammalian characteristics that we can safely regard them as survivals from a period when these stocks were still only at the beginning of their divergence.

Of the two types of existing monotremes the echidna, *Tachyglossus aculeatus*, has been exhibited on many occasions in British and American zoos, and so is comparatively well

The echidna, or spiny anteater

known. The name *Tachyglossus* means 'swift-tongued', and the animal has a long tube-like proboscis, entirely devoid of teeth, which is well adapted to raiding the ants' nests which are the main source of its food. In this, and in the possession of mammalian milk glands, it shows no unusual contrast with the typical anteaters of Central and South America. There, however, the resemblance ends, and a number of unexpected features become apparent. In the first place the echidna is covered with spines instead of fur, and when frightened can roll itself into a ball like a hedgehog; secondly, it possesses the characteristic pouch of the marsupials; thirdly, and most surprising of all, it lays eggs like the oviparous reptiles and the birds. It is as if some irresponsible scientific chef had selected ingredients from several otherwise distinct departments of the animal kingdom and mixed them together to form a bizarre composite creature specially to confound the experts in zoological classification.

The second living monotreme, the duck-billed platypus, *Ornithorhynchus paradoxus*, is more rarely seen outside its own country but, if anything, is even more extraordinary than the echidna. Its scientific name can be translated 'the paradoxical animal with the bird-like snout', and the word platypus itself

The duck-billed platypus

means 'flat-footed', both names being for once admirably descriptive. The animal was first discovered by an English hunter in Queensland in November 1797 who sent its skin to London. In 1799 a description of the skin by George Shaw, Assistant Keeper of the Natural History Department of the British Museum, was published in the *Naturalist's Miscellany*. It was accompanied by a number of excellent coloured illustrations which must certainly have given contemporary naturalists much food for thought. Shaw himself was so astonished by the appearance of the specimen that he was at first disposed to believe that it was a product of human ingenuity, like the notorious 'eastern mermaids' already described in the first part of this book. He writes: 'Of all the Mammalia yet known it seems the most extraordinary in its conformation; exhibiting the perfect resemblance of the beak of a Duck engrafted on the head of a quadruped. So accurate is the similitude that, at first view, it naturally excites the idea of some deceptive preparation by artificial means: the very epidermis, proportion, serratures, manner of opening, and other particulars of the beak of a shoveller, or other broad-billed species of duck, presenting themselves to the view: nor is it without the most minute and rigid examination that we can persuade ourselves of its being the real beak or snout of a quadruped.'

He then proceeds to give a remarkably exact description of the rest of the animal. Its body is much flattened, he says, but otherwise resembles that of a miniature otter about 13 inches long (this estimate of length we now know to be slightly exaggerated, probably due to unnatural stretching of the specimen). The skin is covered with soft, beaver-like fur, 'moderately dark brown above, and of subferruginous white beneath'; the tail is flat and furry like the body, and the feet are webbed; there are five claws on each of the fore-feet, and six on the hind, the extra claw being situated higher up than the rest and projecting like a strong, sharp spur; the eyes are placed on the upper part of the head, but from their size, and the thickness of the fur surrounding them, seem 'but obscurely calculated for distinct vision'.

Shaw concludes: 'When we consider the general form of this animal, and particularly its bill and webbed feet, we shall readily perceive that it must be a resident in watery situations; that it has the habits of digging or burrowing in the banks of rivers, or under ground; and that its food consists of aquatic plants and animals. This is all that can at present be reasonably guessed at: future observations, made in its native regions, will, it is hoped, afford us more ample information, and will make us fully acquainted with the natural history of an animal which differs so widely from all other quadrupeds, and which verifies in a most striking manner the observation of Buffon; viz. that whatever was possible for Nature to produce has actually been produced.'

All this was astonishing enough, but the arrival of several more specimens preserved in spirit still further complicated the zoological puzzle. Already nearly every leading naturalist of the day had felt the urge to advance his own theory on the status of the platypus in the animal kingdom. Those who were chiefly impressed by its furry coat and were prepared to discount the significance of the bill, believed that the creature must be a mammal. Those who took the contrary view were certain that it must be an egg-laying animal whose main affinities were with the reptiles and birds. Now if the mammal theory were correct, it would follow that the platypus must have a uterus, mammary glands and external nipples; if not, these structures would certainly be absent. Not surprisingly, therefore, the rival theorists were in a fever of excitement to know what would be revealed by an examination of the new pickled specimens. The answer came on December 17th 1801 in a paper read before the Royal Society by Sir Everard Home, whom we have already met in connection with the animal of Stronsa. He stated that he could find no trace of the appropriate mammalian organs; on the contrary he had discovered features that lent great support to the egg-laying theory, for the oviducts of the female, instead of combining to form a uterus, opened separately into a cloaca, as in the birds and reptiles.

This news naturally produced great jubilation among the members of the egg-laying school of thought. Their delight was later increased by persistent reports from Australia that the animal in its natural environment was known to lay eggs in burrows in the ground. Unfortunately, however, no one came forward with scientifically acceptable evidence on this point, and in 1824 the great German anatomist J. F. Menckel exploded a new bombshell which gave great support to the opposition. He discovered that the platypus was after all equipped with mammary glands. It appeared that Home had overlooked these because they were exceptionally small and only grew to conspicuous size during the breeding period.

The position was now more complicated than ever. If the platypus was a mammal, why did it have a reproductive system that was apparently designed for the laying of eggs? And if it lay eggs, why did it have the milk glands and nipples of a mammal? The confusion was increased by the fact that there were no confirmed reports of a platypus either laying eggs or suckling its young.

Finally, in 1884, an event occurred which settled the matter once and for all. The Cambridge zoologist W. H. Caldwell went out to New South Wales with the express purpose of studying the breeding habits of the monotremes in their natural environment. And he was fortunate enough to catch both the platypus, and its relative the echidna, in the very act of laying their eggs. He was so delighted with this discovery that he immediately sent a telegram to Montreal where the British Association for the Advancement of Science was in session. It read simply 'Monotremes oviparous, ovum meroblastic – CALDWELL.' With this laconic message from the other side of the Earth there ended a scientific controversy which had lasted nearly a hundred years. Fortunately, also, both parties to the dispute could claim to have gained peace with honour. The platypus had conveniently proved them both partially right. Not only did it first produce its young in an external egg, but after the eggs had been hatched it nourished them, like other mammals, at the breast.

As we have already said, both marsupials and monotremes are evidently survivors from a comparatively early period in the development of land life. They have retained features that are characteristic of a far more primitive level of development than those found in the placental mammals that now dominate the Earth. This being so, we may well ask how they have managed to survive for so long. The answer lies not so much in zoology as in palaeogeography, the science that studies the former distribution of the surface features of the globe.

Students of palaeogeography have deduced that in past ages the outlines of the continents and oceans were very different from what they are today. At the beginning of the Age of Reptiles, for example, a great land mass known as Gondwanaland (or, more correctly, Gondwana, for the word 'wana' means land in Sanskrit), extended right across the area now covered by the Indian and South Atlantic Oceans, and the Australian, African and South American continents. This was the largest continuous land mass in the geological history of the Earth, a Southern Continent far vaster, and containing far stranger forms of life, than any dreamed of by the early human pioneers of exploration and travel.

But contrary to popular belief, the surface features of the Earth are not fixed for all time, and few things are more impermanent than the eternal hills of the romantic poets. Sometime towards the end of the Jurassic Period, Gondwanaland began to break up. By the dawn of the Cenozoic Era, when the mammals were embarking on their period of evolutionary domination, there was not a single Southern Continent, but three great islands corresponding respectively with modern South America, Africa and Australia.

The mechanics of the disintegration are still controversial. Many geologists are inclined to believe that Gondwanaland broke up due to the subsidence of the present ocean basins; others, less conservative, are supporters of the theory of continental drift. This most poetic and revolutionary of modern geological theories was worked out by the German geophysicist Alfred Lothar Wegener in the second decade of the present century. Wegener believed that the continents were not solidly rooted in fixed positions on the surface of the Earth, but floated more or less freely on the denser materials lying below. They were thus capable of horizontal movements on a formerly unsuspected scale. In support of his theory he pointed to the fact that the present continents, if one imagined them pushed together as in the map on the opposite page, would fit like the pieces of a jig-saw puzzle. This in turn led him to suggest that all the continents of the modern world were once united and had simply drifted apart.

The objections to the theory are numerous and formidable, and the great controversy it has aroused can be studied in detail in some of the books listed in the Bibliography. But whether we prefer to regard Wegener as a scientific prophet or simply as a poetic dreamer, there is overwhelming palaeontological evidence for the fact that the three southern continents were once somehow connected by dry land. When this was so, of course, the ancestral continent formed a single theatre of evolution, with each species influencing and being influenced by its neighbours over the whole area according to the laws of natural selection. But when the land mass split up there was a tendency for evolution to continue along different lines in the three separate parts. Actually this did not everywhere lead to such completely isolated communities as one might expect. Land bridges were intermittently formed between South America and North America, and between Africa and Eurasia, while

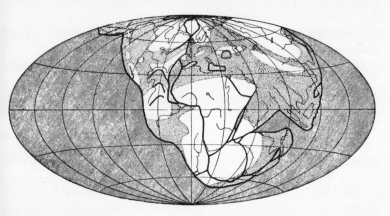

Map showing how the world may have looked 230 million years ago, before the separation of the continents. From *The Origin of Continents and Oceans* by Alfred Wegener. (Reproduced by permission of Messrs Methuen Ltd.)

the northern continents were themselves joined together for many millions of years at what are now the Bering Straits. Thus the only large inhabited land-mass to remain completely unlinked to the rest of the world was Australia. And while the complicated interplay of evolutionary factors continued elsewhere much as before, the life of Australia developed in a closed system, largely unaffected by outside influences.

We can now begin to understand why Australia is unique in its possession of so many ancient forms of life. Cut off from the rest of the world, its inhabitants were not called upon to make nearly such radical adaptations as were necessary in other regions where competition was stronger. Thus early mammalian forms such as the monotremes and marsupials continued to flourish in Australia, when elsewhere they were superseded by the more efficient placental mammals. In fact the American opossum is the only primitive marsupial to have retained a good foothold outside the Australasian region. And this must surely be because it is a small, insignificant creature, adapted to a tree-dwelling and nocturnal life which largely helps to keep it out of harm's way.

Now if the strangely primitive fauna of Australia has survived as a result of a long period of geographical isolation, we may be led to think that the process can continue so long as the continent remains unlinked by land with any other region. But this is not so. With the evolution of man, and his discovery of sea transport, geographical barriers begin to be broken down. Already, many thousands of years ago, the arrival of the aborigines in Australia from south-eastern Asia had begun to change the ecology of the continent. Ecologically speaking, aboriginal man was a new predator who came at once into competition with the marsupial occupants of the region. Moreover he brought with him his domestic dog, which soon began to run wild; this advanced placental mammal, now known as the dingo, was to become almost as dangerous to the native animal population as man himself. Later ages saw the introduction of further new species, such as the fox and the domestic cat, so that the security of the primitive marsupials and monotremes became increasingly threatened. In fact man and his importations were soon beginning to set at naught the advantages of geographical isolation which the Australian fauna had previously enjoyed.

In the title of this chapter I have referred to the Australian region as the attic of the Earth, and certainly at the present day it is still the home of a unique array of ancient animals. These include not only individual species entitled to rank as living fossils but whole classes, orders and families that have survived from a remote period in geological time. The breaking down of geographical boundaries by man is now threatening these interesting relics of the past. *Homo sapiens* has shown too often that the by-product of his own evolutionary success is the extinction of many of his fellow inhabitants of the Earth. Whether the greater wisdom now shown in some quarters, particularly in Australia itself, will enable the existing species of marsupials and monotremes to be preserved remains to be seen. Meanwhile, in the last part of this book, I shall speak of some of the animals that have already disappeared for ever from the Earth during man's brief period of domination.

PART FOUR

The Death of Races

CHAPTER FIFTEEN

The Last of the Quaggas

Afar in the Desert I love to ride,
With the silent Bush-boy alone by my side:
O'er the brown Karroo where the bleating cry
Of the springbok's fawn sounds plaintively;
And the timorous quagga's shrill whistling neigh
Is heard by the fountain at twilight grey.

THOMAS PRINGLE: *Afar in the Desert* (1828)

... and sometimes, though rarely, may be seen an isolated tumulus, riding, like a ship at her cable, in a floating sea of deceitful mirage, which causes the gay glittering coats of the Quagga to sparkle like mica.

SIR WILLIAM CORNWALLIS HARRIS:
Portraits of the Game and Wild Animals of Southern Africa (1840)

THERE is a terrible finality about the word extinction. The death of individuals, even of our own species, we have learnt to accept, comforting ourselves with the thought that our immortality lies, if not in heaven, at least in the vigour that we can pass on to future generations. But the death of whole races or kinds of animals inspires an altogether more melancholy emotion. We are appalled and saddened not only by the loss of beautiful and vital forms of life, but by the tremendous waste of evolutionary energy that is involved in the extinction of even the humblest race of living things. This is especially true of animals that have become extinct during our own epoch, and whose last survivors may actually have died within living memory. And if we are reflective people we must be saddened most of all by the thought that man himself has too often played a prominent role in the final tragedy.

In this chapter I want to tell the story of the quagga, one of the most splendid and beautiful examples of African game. Originally plentiful throughout the Orange Free State, Cape Province (or Cape Colony as it then was) and neighbouring parts of South Africa, it suffered in less than a century a catastrophic decline. This culminated in 1882 in the death of the last quagga in the world, a captive in the Amsterdam Zoological Gardens.

For those who may not know what the quagga was like, a word or two must be devoted to its description. It was a member of the horse family, belonging to the same group as the zebras, but distinguished from them by its peculiar markings. The typical zebra is of course characterized by its prominent black and white stripes. These may be narrow, as in the beautiful Grevy's zebra of Abyssinia and Somaliland, or comparatively broad as in Grant's zebra and other varieties living further south. In these kinds of zebra the stripes cover the whole body from head to tail, but in the quagga they were only clearly distinguishable on the head and neck, the forequarters being lightly and indistinctly marked, and the rest of the body a plain chestnut brown with white legs and a white tail. The quagga was also more thickset and stocky than the more northerly varieties of zebra, its proportions resembling those of a pony rather than a horse.

In its wild state the quagga seems to have been primarily an animal of the plains. An average herd consisted of between twenty-five and forty individuals, and the animals were frequently found in company with the ostrich and the white-tailed gnu. In summer they must have made a magnificent sight grazing over the flower-covered plains which extended in all directions to an unbroken horizon. Travellers report that frequently many herds of quagga were visible at the same time on these plains, dotted about at intervals like fishing fleets on a multi-coloured sea.

The history of the quagga is comparatively short. Although zebras were known to the Romans as long ago as the second century A.D., being referred to by the historian Cassius Dio as 'Horses of the Sun which resemble tigers', the quagga does not make its first authentic entry into European literature until 1758. In that year George Edwards, naturalist and librarian of the Royal College of Physicians, published his picturesque *Gleanings of Natural History*, in the first volume of which there appeared a splendid coloured picture of the quagga, identified, however, as a female zebra. Edwards writes: 'This curious animal was brought alive, together with the male, from the Cape of Good Hope: the male dying before they arrived at

London, I did not see it; but this female lived several years at a house of his Royal Highness the Prince of Wales, at Kew. . . . The noise it made was much different from that of an ass, resembling more the confused barking of a mastiff-dog. It seemed to be of a savage and fierce nature: no one would venture to approach it, but a gardener in the Prince's service, who was used to feed it, and could mount on its back. I saw it eat a large paper of tobacco, paper and all; and I was told, it would eat flesh, or any kind of food they would give it. I suppose that proceeded from necessity, or habit, in its long sea-voyage; for it undoubtedly feeds naturally much as horses and asses do, I mean on vegetables.'

Buffon made the same mistake of taking the quagga for a female zebra, and illustrated it as such in the supplement to his *Histoire des Animaux Quadrupèdes* published in 1787. But as British and Dutch travellers penetrated further into the interior of South Africa, and its natural history became better known, the quagga was generally recognized as a distinct species. Nevertheless several interesting points were made in these eighteenth century descriptions, notably Edwards' account of its cry as resembling the barking of a mastiff-dog. This seems to have been quite accurate, for the very name of the animal was derived from its characteristic call; this was rendered in the onomatopoeic syllables *khoua-khoua* by the Hottentots, and was later adopted by the Boers in the form quakka or quagga.

Several early travellers brought back interesting descriptions of the quagga from its native land. One of the best accounts comes from the Swedish naturalist Andrew Sparrman, who made a journey into the country of the Hottentots in 1775. The record of his adventures was translated into English in the 1780s and it shows Sparrman to have been a man of considerable intelligence, charm and humour. How, for instance, can one resist chapter synopses that contain such headings as these: 'Hires a bastard, a man of family, for his guide. Is lodged and entertained by a slave. Curious method of serving at the same time God and mammon. The author very ungallantly neglects to requite the services of a female slave. A slave's revenge on his niggardly master. The author in danger at a rich widow's house of being kicked out of doors, on his hat being discovered with the brim stuck full of beetles. Floats naked over the river to an islet on a bundle of palmites plants, in order to botanize there. Makes a sexton and his wife happy by prognosticating the death of the latter. . . .' And so on, in the same vein.

Sparrman first came across quaggas at Swellendam near the river Breede, and realized at once that they were a race quite distinct from the other zebras. He was particularly impressed by a quagga that had been caught when young by the natives and brought up as a pet. This animal, he remarked, was ex-

Quagga on the South African plains

ceedingly tame, and also quite unafraid of the hyenas that inhabited those parts. For this reason it was turned out at night with the horses, for whom it made a most efficient guard.

The traveller William Burchell, after whom Burchell's zebra is named, was another early writer who brought back interesting reports of the quagga. On his journey into the interior of South Africa in 1811 and 1812 he observed vast numbers of quaggas and remarked that they were frequently shot to provide food for the native slaves. Burchell himself does not seem to have had a very high opinion of the meat, saying 'though much praised, I felt no desire to make a meal of it.' However on one occasion he was so impressed by the obvious relish with which his Hottentots were eating the meat that he ordered a quagga steak for his own dinner. Rather grudgingly he remarks: 'The novelty, and my own curiosity, must have had some influence on this occasion, since I was induced to consider it good and palatable. It was tender, and possessed a taste which seemed to be between beef and mutton.'

The shooting of the quagga by travellers and the Dutch

colonists to provide a supply of meat for their servants was the main cause of its sudden decline. Its skin was also used by the Boers for making the home-made shoes known as *velschoons*, the thicker portions covering the angle of the hocks being especially prized for this purpose. Sir William Cornwallis Harris, writing in 1840, reported that 'the animal was formerly extremely common within the Colony, but vanishing before the strides of civilization, is now to be found in very limited numbers, and on the borders only.' Outside Cape Colony, however, he reported a more cheerful state of affairs. In the as yet uninvaded wilderness to the north, 'on those sultry plains which are completely taken possession of by wild beasts, and may with strict propriety be termed the domains of savage nature, it occurs in interminable herds. . . . Moving slowly across the profile of the ocean-like horizon, uttering a shrill barking neigh, of which its name forms a correct imitation, long files of Quaggas continually remind the early traveller of a rival caravan on its march.'

Twenty-five years after these words were written the quagga was extinct in Cape Province and only lingered elsewhere in isolated groups. The main period of destruction began in 1850 when the Boer farmers, venturing further and further into the interior, began a merciless massacre of the surviving quaggas to obtain their meat and skins. In addition to their use in the manufacture of shoes the skins were employed for a variety of other purposes, including the making of sacks for transporting grain. No close season was observed, and mares, stallions and foals fell indiscriminately to the hunters' guns. To increase the possibilities of slaughter it is even reported that the Boers removed the bullets from the dead quarry so that they could be reconditioned and used a second time. By about 1870 the wild quagga was completely extinct.

During the hundred years or so before the extinction of the quagga, sixteen specimens are known to have been brought alive to Europe. Some of these seem to have been quite tame, and on more than one occasion were broken to harness. Sparrman had already described seeing a quagga being driven in a team of five horses in South Africa, and in 1827 the editors of the English edition of Cuvier's *Régne Animal* wrote: 'The Couaggas are easily tamed, and rendered subservient to domestic uses: and in confirmation of this assertion it may be observed that among the equipages occasionally exhibited in the gay season in Hyde Park, and other fashionable places of resort, may be seen a curricle drawn by two Couaggas, which seem as subservient to the curb and whip as any well-trained horses.' These two animals were apparently the pride of a certain Mr Sheriff Parkins, who must have made a minor sensation when out on his Sunday morning drive. When these quaggas died, sometime about 1830, their skulls passed into the hands of a private collector and ended up in the museum of the Royal College of Surgeons.

Another famous quagga imported into Europe lived for several years in the Jardin des Plantes in Paris; it was sixteen when it arrived and is believed to have died of old age. On occasions it could be handled with impunity, but if frightened or excited – as when it was moved from one enclosure to another – it would bite and kick fiercely with nervous rage. In such moods it was essential to give it a very wide berth, for quaggas, despite their usual mildness, were quite large enough to inflict serious wounds. Sir William Cornwallis Harris recalls meeting a native who had lost all the fingers of his right hand from the vicious bite of a quagga stallion. And he also tells how one of his Hottentot followers, when in an amiable mood, would describe the death of his brother (who rejoiced, incidentally, in the name of Phoebus Cockerlockie) from the kick of a wounded quagga. In this episode Harris comments dryly: 'Had the cranium of the luckless deceased possessed but one third the solidity of that of his surviving relative, this catastrophe could scarcely have occurred.'

The London Zoo possessed three quaggas at different times during the nineteenth century. One of these, a female purchased in 1851, lived in the Zoo for 21 years, and is remarkable as being the only quagga ever to have been photographed alive. For a time it was accompanied by a stallion, but in 1864 the male animal unfortunately injured itself in a fit of rage and had to be destroyed. The wild quagga was at this time already doomed, and it is sad to reflect that but for this accident it might have been possible to establish a semi-domesticated herd in captivity.

But the London Zoo quagga was not the last of its kind.

When it died in 1872 there was at least one other quagga alive in Europe, the famous specimen at the Amsterdam Zoological Gardens. There may also have been another at Antwerp, the survivor of a shipment, the last ever to be made, which reached Europe about 1870 from M. Bols, the Belgian Consul at Port Elizabeth; and despite the fact that no wild quaggas had been reported for several years it is just possible that a few individuals still lingered on in remote corners of South Africa. By 1875 or 1876, however, there is little doubt that the animal in the Amsterdam Zoo had the melancholy distinction of being the last living quagga in the world. It had been purchased by the Amsterdam Zoological Society in 1867, probably from the Antwerp Zoo, where a fine specimen is known to have lived for several years prior to M. Bols' importation. It lived on for another ten years after the death of the London Zoo specimen, and finally died, thereby extinguishing its race, on August 12th 1882.

There is, however, a postscript to the quagga story. In 1917 Major C. N. Manning, the first Resident Commissioner of Ovamboland, while on a trek through the Kaoko Veld of South West Africa, saw a herd of an unusual kind of zebra, brownish in colour and incompletely striped. Unfortunately he had no binoculars with him, and as the animals were at a distance and too timid to be approached, he was unable to obtain a satisfactory view of them. However, on his return to Ovamboland he reported the matter to Mr C. H. Hahn, the Native Commissioner, with a request that he should make investigations.

Shortly after this interesting observation, further reports began to come in from other sources, all describing the same kind of animal. Hahn found some of these so convincing that it seemed almost impossible to explain them away. He was encouraged to believe that there must be a previously undiscovered species of zebra in the Kaoko Veld, or at least a number of unusual hybrids. For some time he even dared to believe that the impossible had happened, and that a herd of previously unlocated quagga might still exist in this remote and barren region of South Africa.

But these hopes were doomed to disappointment, for an intensive investigation failed to reveal any reliable confirmatory evidence. Although on at least one occasion a native tribe made positive statements that such animals had been frequently seen and actually lived in the neighbourhood, further questioning always revealed that the animals referred to were either Burchell's zebra or Hartmann's mountain zebra, both sub-species already well known to naturalists. Hahn was finally convinced that the animals seen by Manning and other observers were simply specimens of the mountain zebra, *Equus zebra hartmannae*, distorted by heat haze. In support of this opinion he writes: 'In the hot season, generally at midday, with the sun overhead Hartmann's Zebra from a distance resemble dark brown donkeys. When the heat haze is severe, it is difficult, at times impossible, to discern the dark markings without the aid of binoculars. I have personally experienced this difficulty on more than one occasion.'

Since Manning's report of 1917 there have been several further rumours that the quagga is still alive in the Kaoko Veld. One of these, originating in a report by a Mr de Pimental Teixeira, was investigated as recently as 1940. We cannot help feeling, however, that such rumours, which always lead to the same blank result, spring from a forlorn hope. There can now be no doubt that man has finally wiped the quagga from the face of the Earth.

CHAPTER SIXTEEN

The Story of a Massacre

We human beings are seemingly so indifferent to the death of one
of our own kind that for us to give thought to the death of a bird
appears strange indeed. Yet thousands of people took serious and
melancholy notice of the death of a certain bird back in 1914. . . .
Its death marked the close of what was perhaps Nature's greatest
dynasty of birds. Its history is one of thoughtless destruction and
ruthless persecution without parallel.

ROY L. ABBOTT: *Natural History* Vol. 53 (1944)

IN the years immediately before the First World War, visitors
to the Zoological Gardens at Cincinnati in the State of Ohio,
U.S.A. had the opportunity to enjoy a unique and moving
experience. In an outside aviary, inconspicuously placed
among the other exhibits, could be seen a solitary female bird,
delicately marked in grey and reddish brown, which obviously
belonged to the pigeon family. Those who were interested in
such things could learn from the label that this was a specimen
of *Ectopistes migratorius*, the passenger pigeon, and that having
been bred in the Gardens about 1885, it was over 25 years old.
The more imaginative visitors must also have felt a kind of
poignant wonder to discover that it was beyond all reasonable
doubt the last of its kind.

The Cincinnati passenger pigeon died at 1 p.m. on September
1st 1914. This happens, incidentally, to be the only occasion on
which the exact moment of the extinction of a species has been
recorded. The body was packed in ice and despatched forthwith to the United States National Museum in Washington
where its obsequies were marked by a similar chronological
precision. According to Dr R. W. Schufeldt, who dissected the
bird, the body arrived in Washington with commendable
promptitude early the following morning. At 11 a.m. it was
photographed in three positions in the Museum studio, and at
a few minutes to 4 p.m., after Mr William Palmer had skinned
it for the taxidermist, Dr Schufeldt began his dissection. He
found that the bird was not in a diseased condition and had

probably died of old age. The stuffed skin was preserved in the Museum's Bird Gallery, where it can still be seen to this day.

But the interest of the passenger pigeon is not comprised in such melancholy statistics. It lies in the appalling and shameful record of human callousness and folly which brought the species to its end. This story has been told before, but I make no excuse for telling it again; each repetition may perhaps do something to emphasize the danger which threatens several equally interesting species today.

The passenger pigeon was once not only common, but the best known bird in the whole of North America. It was larger than other American pigeons, some specimens exceeding one and a half feet in length from beak to tail. It was conspicuous also by its colour, the male having the upper part of the head, the back and wings coloured a delicate shade of blue, while below, the throat and breast were reddish fawn, shading to white on the abdomen. The female was less vividly marked, but the distribution of the colours was the same; she was a smaller and somewhat more subdued replica of her mate.

The first recorded observations of the passenger pigeon go back to the sixteenth century when the French navigator Jacques Cartier reported seeing them on the banks of the river St. Lawrence, which he discovered in 1534. All the early writers were impressed by the vast numbers of the birds, which frequently congregated together and could be seen flying overhead on their migrations in a never-ending stream. As early as 1605 the French explorer Samuel de Champlain was talking of 'an infinite number of Pigeons' he had seen along the coast of Maine, while Josselyn, another Frenchman, wrote in 1672: 'I have seen a flight of pigeons that to my thinking had neither beginning nor ending, length nor breadth, and so thick I could not see the sun.'

Such an extraordinary phenomenon was bound soon to attract the attention of professional naturalists, who endorsed the reports of the early observers. For example, Mark Catesby, writing in 1731 in *The Natural History of Carolina, Florida and the Bahama Islands*, said: 'Of these pigeons there come in Winter to *Virginia* and *Carolina*, from the North, incredible Numbers; insomuch that in some places where they roost (which they do on one another's Backs) they often break down the limbs of

Oaks with their weight, and leave their Dung some Inches thick under the Trees they roost on. Where they light, they so effectually clear the Woods of Acorns and other Mast, that the Hogs that come after them, to the detriment of the Planters, fare very poorly. In *Virginia* I have seen them fly in such continued trains three days successively, that there was not the least Interval in losing sight of them, but that some where or other in the Air they were to be seen continuing their flight South. . . . In their passage the People of *New York* and *Philadelphia* shoot many of them as they fly, from their Balconies and Tops of Houses; and in *New-England* there are such Numbers, that with long Poles they knock them down from their Roosts in the Night in great numbers.'

Alexander Wilson, in his *American Ornithology*, published in the early nineteenth century, adds further interesting details to the story. He tells how after the pigeons have occupied the same spot for several days the entire area is devastated for many thousands of acres. The ground is littered with broken boughs which have collapsed under the birds' weight, the air is heavy with the stench emanating from the great mounds of dung, and even the trees themselves are 'killed as completely as if girdled with an axe'. It is often not until many years later that vegetation begins to creep back into the desolate wilderness which the passing of the birds has created.

In addition to journeying and roosting together the passenger pigeons used to breed at communal nesting sites. These were even vaster in extent than the roosts. Wilson gives an account of one nesting site at Shelbyville in Kentucky that covered an area of at least 120 square miles. 'In this tract', he writes, 'almost every tree was furnished with nests, wherever the branches could accomodate them. . . . As soon as the young were fully grown, and before they left the nests, numerous parties of the inhabitants, from all parts of the adjacent country, came with waggons, axes, beds, cooking utensils, many of them accompanied by the greater part of their families, and encamped for several days at this immense nursery. Several of them informed me, that the noise in the woods was so great as to terrify their horses, and that it was difficult for one person to hear another speak without bawling in his ear. The ground was strewed with broken limbs of trees, eggs, and young squab Pigeons, which had been precipitated from above, and on which herds of hogs were fattening. Hawks, Buzzards and Eagles were sailing about in great numbers, and seizing the squabs from their nests at pleasure; while from twenty feet upwards to the tops of the trees the view through the woods presented a perpetual tumult of crowding and fluttering multitudes of pigeons, their wings roaring like thunder.'

It would be possible to multiply such observations indefinitely, but I shall limit myself to one more quotation, this time from *The Birds of America* by the famous American ornithologist John James Audubon. This is particularly interesting in recording the impression made on a trained naturalist by the sight of the pigeons in the air.

He writes:

In the autumn of 1813, I left my house at Henderson, on the banks of the Ohio, on my way to Louisville. In passing over the Barrens a few miles beyond Hardensburgh, I observed the Pigeons flying from north-east to south-west, in greater numbers than I thought I had ever seen them before . . . . The air was literally filled with Pigeons; the light of noon-day was obscured as by an eclipse; the dung fell in spots, not unlike melting flakes of snow; and the continued buzz of wings had a tendency to lull my senses to repose.

Whilst waiting for dinner at YOUNG's inn at the confluence of Salt river with the Ohio, I saw, at my leisure, immense legions still going by, with a front reaching far beyond the Ohio on the west, and the beechwood forests directly on the east of me. . . . I cannot describe to you the extreme beauty of their aerial evolutions, when a Hawk chanced to press upon the rear of a flock. At once, like a torrent, and with a noise like thunder, they rushed into a compact mass, pressing upon each other towards the centre. In these almost solid masses, they darted forward in undulating and angular lines, descended and swept close over the earth with inconceivable velocity, mounted perpendicularly so as to resemble a vast column, and, when high, were seen wheeling and twisting within their continued lines, which then resembled the coils of a gigantic serpent.

Before sunset I reached Louisville, distant from Hardensburgh fifty-five miles. The Pigeons were still passing in undiminished numbers; and continued to do so for three days in succession. The people were all in arms. The banks of the Ohio were crowded with men and boys, incessantly shooting at the pilgrims, which there flew lower as they passed the river. Multitudes were thus destroyed.

For a week or more, the population fed on no other flesh than that of Pigeons, and talked of nothing but Pigeons.

These great migrations were apparently caused entirely by the search for new feeding grounds, seeming to have no seasonal connection with the climate or with the pigeons' breeding habits. When we consider the prodigious numbers of birds that must have composed such flights it seems almost incredible that just over a hundred years after Audubon penned his description the passenger pigeon was extinct. No naturalist of the early nineteenth century had even contemplated such a possibility. Despite the many thousands of birds shot for food or for gain there was no noticeable sign of any decrease in their ranks.

But the slaughter was on a scale that no species could indefinitely sustain. The birds' unfortunate habit of congregating in vast numbers at their roosts and nesting sites made them an easy prey for the hunter. Also each pigeon normally laid only one, or at most two eggs, so that despite their enormous numbers the gaps in their ranks were not being adequately refilled.

So far I have only mentioned the slaughter of the passenger pigeon by men as an incidental to descriptions of its communal habits. But to understand the truly sensational decline of such an enormous dynasty of birds we must examine the details of the massacre a little more closely. The sad story began almost as soon as the pigeon was discovered, Champlain himself remarking in 1607 that he and his men took 'a great many' of them for the pot. For the next two hundred years it was a common practice for vast numbers of birds to be destroyed every time they settled to roost or breed. By the nineteenth century the orgy of slaughter had reached its peak, many millions of birds being slain each year.

Audubon records that in 1805 he saw schooners laden with huge quantities of dead pigeons from the Hudson river docking at New York where the birds were sold at a cent apiece. Twenty-five years later they were so abundant in the markets of New York that piles of them met the eye in every direction. Varied techniques were used for catching such enormous numbers of birds. Guns, of course, accounted for a good many, while others were netted or clubbed. Pigeon hunting became a full-time occupation and its practitioners moved from one breeding ground to another, slaughtering many thousands of pigeons a day. Audubon knew one man in Pennsylvania who caught and killed upwards of 500 dozen pigeons a day, netting sometimes as many as twenty dozen in one throw of his net. A particularly revolting practice was the cutting down of trees to collect the young squabs, each tree always being felled so that it would bring down two or three others with it to save the hunters unnecessary labour. By these means between three and four hundred squabs could sometimes be gathered by felling a single tree.

Although the price obtained for each pigeon was originally low it mounted as people obtained a taste for the meat. In the Eastern United States pigeons were soon fetching between $1.00 and $1.50 a dozen. With the increasing profit of the trade still more efficient means were devised for intensifying the slaughter. Acres of ground were baited with grain, and when the area was covered with thousands of unsuspecting pigeons huge nets were used to catch over a thousand birds at a time. The more enterprising killers brought small cannons and swivel guns into play which could scatter a pound or more of small shot at a single discharge. Each burst from the gun or throw of the net produced enough birds to fetch a minimum of $90 on the New York market, where the demand for pigeons sometimes exceeded a hundred barrels a day.

But not all the captured birds were immediately slaughtered. One of the favourite sports in America in the eighties of the last century was live pigeon shooting. Thousands of pigeons were kept cooped up in boxes for weeks for these gallant occasions, to be released eventually as targets for the guns. Dr Abbott has recorded that at one such orgy held at Coney Island in 1881 no fewer than 20,000 pigeons were offered up as a sacrifice to the brave sportsmen. The crowning irony is that this meeting was held under the auspices of the New York Association for the Protection of Fish and Game.

Writing in 1892, in a Special Bulletin of the Smithsonian Institution devoted to the life histories of North American Birds, Captain Charles Bendire describes the closing stages in the passenger pigeon's decline. We learn from him that as recently as 1878, despite all the depredations of the killers, the bird still existed in vast numbers. This was the year of the great

7a Passenger pigeons in Wisconsin, by Walter Thorp. From a
pencil and watercolour in the University of Wisconsin, reproduced by kind permission of Walter E. Scott

7b Shooting passenger pigeons in northern Louisiana, by
Smith Bennett, from *The Illustrated Sporting and Dramatic News*
(1875)

8 Martha, the last living passenger pigeon, which died at
1 p.m. on September 1st 1914. (Reproduced by kind permission
of the Zoological Society of Cincinnati)

nesting at Petovsky in Michigan, which covered an area about 40 miles long and between 3 and 10 miles in width. Bendire quotes a report by Professor Roney in the *Chicago Field*, in which he says of this nesting: 'The number of dead birds sent by rail was estimated at 12,500 daily, or 1,500,000 for the summer, besides 80,352 live birds; an equal number was sent by water. We have, adding the thousands of dead and wounded ones not secured, and the myriads of squabs left dead in the nest, at the lowest possible estimate, a grand total of 1,000,000,000 Pigeons sacrificed to Mammon during the nesting of 1878.' Even if we admit that this last figure is considerably exaggerated, we can see that no species could withstand for very many more years such a ruthless onslaught on its resources.

In the following decade smaller nestings were reported from several areas, but pigeon hunting gradually declined for lack of birds. Two nestings took place in Michigan in 1881, another in Pennsylvania in 1886, while in Canada the birds bred in considerable numbers in Manitoba in 1887. But the damage had been done, and the passenger pigeon was by now destined to an inescapable doom. Despite certain desultory efforts to protect the survivors, the nineties saw the pigeon reduced to a few scattered flocks and individuals. Thus a flock was seen in Illinois in 1895 and others during the next year or two in Wisconsin, Nebraska and a few other states, mainly in the west of the country. The last small flock to be seen consisted of about fifty individuals in Michigan, and the last recorded wild pigeon was apparently that killed in Quebec in 1907. The few remaining birds in captivity died during the next few years, until the only survivor was the solitary hen at Cincinnati.

The sequence of inhuman acts that led to the extinction of this beautiful race of birds is so disturbing to the imagination that it is not surprising that men have cast around for reasons to exonerate them from full responsibility. During the last forty years numerous theories have been proposed to account for the annihilation of the species. Some have said that thousands of the birds perished by drowning in the Gulf of Mexico on an unexplained migration to South America; others that the species was struck by an unexpected epidemic. It has also been suggested that the destruction of forests to make way for advancing civilization partially explained the disappearance of the bird. Certainly some of the factors suggested may have accounted for the loss of a few hundreds or even thousands of pigeons during the last years of their existence. But the main cause of their extinction is plain for all to see. Man cannot escape the moral responsibility for the callousness, the greed, and the supreme irreverence for life that led to the passing of the passenger pigeon.

CHAPTER SEVENTEEN

Steller and the Great Sea-Cow

Along the whole shore of the island, especially where streams
flow into the sea and all kinds of seaweed are most abundant, the
sea-cow 'morskaya korova', so called by our Russians, occurs at all
seasons of the year in great numbers and in herds.

GEORG WILHELM STELLER: *Journal* (1742)

He shall return no more to his house, neither shall his place know
him any more.

JOB: *Ch.* 7, *v.* 10

AT 4 a.m. on Thursday June 4th 1741, the packet boat
St. Peter set sail from the harbour of Petropavlovsk on the
Kamchatka peninsula of eastern Siberia. The ship, which
flew the Russian flag, was under the command of the great
Danish navigator Vitus Bering, the object of the voyage being
to explore the northernmost limits of the Pacific Ocean, and
especially to discover whether there was a land connection
between Siberia and the American continent. The commander
and nearly half the crew never returned to Russian soil again.

On board the *St. Peter*, numbered among the complement of
seventy-eight men, was the German physician and naturalist
Georg Wilhelm Steller. He had been asked by Bering to join
the expedition at the last moment because of the illness of the
chief surgeon, Dr Kaspar Feige. It was also thought that his
experience as a mineralogist would enable him to assess the
mining possibilities in the new lands it was hoped to discover.

The first part of the voyage went well. Bering made a successful landfall on the west coast of Alaska, where Steller was the
first naturalist ever to set foot. Although only allowed ashore
for a few hours he made an impressive list of the various kinds
of animals and plants he observed, and even discovered a new
species of jay, which was later named after him *Cyanocitta stelleri*.
On his return to the ship he records that Bering brewed him a
cup of chocolate, then a rare and precious beverage, in re-
cognition of his being the first European to spend a day on
Alaskan soil.

But after this auspicious opening the voyage turned to tragedy. The ship had no sooner left on the return journey when scurvy, that most dreaded enemy of the early explorers, broke out among the crew. The condition of the victims was aggravated by bad water taken on board at the Shumagin Islands, and by October the effects of the disease had begun to interfere seriously with the working of the ship. The anguish of the crew was further increased by gales and head winds which drove them hundreds of miles back on their course.

At length, on November 4th, a high, inhospitable coast loomed through the fog ahead, which the sailors at first joyfully believed to be the Siberian mainland. But after an observation of the sun it was realized that they were still many hundreds of miles from home, and the crew's elation turned to despair. A conference was called, and as only six casks of bad water were left, it was decided by general consent to go ashore. By this time there were not even enough able-bodied men to leave a skeleton crew on board, and the ship had to be completely abandoned. The sick were installed in improvised huts and dug-outs in the sand, and a week later the *St. Peter* broke its cable and was piled on the beach by a north-easterly gale, a badly damaged wreck.

It was in these dramatic circumstances that Steller discovered the animal that forms the subject of this chapter. Sea-otters and foxes were in evidence as soon as the boats came to the shore, the latter being so tame that they ran up to the men and sniffed and snapped at them. But Steller also observed in the water at high tide a number of huge hump-backed shapes like overturned boats moving about. A few days later, when he obtained a better view of the creatures, he realized that they belonged to a previously unknown genus; they were the animals now known to science as *Rhytina stelleri*, or Steller's sea-cow.

Before we give a fuller account of this interesting discovery a word or two must be said about the fate of the ill-starred expedition. On Tuesday December 8th 1741 Bering died of scurvy complicated by other diseases which Steller diagnosed as dropsy and gas gangrene. Several other members of the crew had previously succumbed at sea, and further deaths in the next few weeks brought the total number of casualties to over thirty. But then things began to take a turn for the better. The health of the party was improved by fresh food and water, and soon the men were able to begin the work of rebuilding the shattered *St. Peter*. After seven months of continuous labour they had a new and serviceable vessel in which they successfully completed the voyage to Petropavlovsk. Steller himself was not, however,

Steller's sea-cow. From an eighteenth century chart

destined to make a personal report of his discoveries to the Academy of Sciences in St. Petersburg. After many adventures in Siberia, including a period of wrongful imprisonment, he died of fever in Tyumen on November 12th 1746.

In the midst of the privations and hardships of this story-book expedition we can only marvel at the extraordinary single-mindedness that enabled Steller to make daily records of his scientific observations. And it is particularly fortunate that he was present at the discovery of the northern sea-cow, for he is the only trained observer ever to have seen it alive. Thirty years after the survivors of the Alaskan expedition returned to Kamchatka it is doubtful whether more than a handful of the creatures survived. Certainly the species became totally extinct sometime during the nineteenth century.

The northern sea-cow was a relation of the manatee and the dugong described in the first chapter of this book. But compared to them it was a veritable giant, measuring from 25 to 30 feet long and weighing anything up to 3½ tons. Considering the immense bulk of its body the head was remarkably small, with mobile lips, the upper one being covered with an impressive array of white bristles the thickness of chickens' quills. It pulled itself through the shallows with the aid of two stump-like paws situated at the forward end of its trunk; there were no hind limbs, but in deeper water the animal propelled itself by vertical strokes of its huge double fluked tail. The skin was not smooth as in manatees and dugongs, but corrugated into a number of ridges and wrinkles; hence the scientific name *Rhytina stelleri*, which literally translated means 'Steller's wrinkled one'.

The range of *Rhytina* was restricted to the islands now known as the Commander Group – namely, Copper Island, where the crew of the *St. Peter* were cast away, and the larger Bering Island to the west. It is particularly surprising that the animals were found in these icy waters when one remembers that their only relatives are restricted entirely to the warm tropic seas. But their stout bark-like hide doubtless helped them to retain their body heat, and they were additionally protected by the thick layer of blubber which underlay it. Apparently they never ventured far from the shore, for they were said to be unable to dive deeply for their food, while in the open sea they would also have been an easy prey for killer whales. They were entirely vegetarian, browsing like great herds of marine cattle on the lush North Pacific seaweeds, which flourish in this region in the most lavish abundance.

Steller gives such an interesting and readable account of the habits of *Rhytina* which I will quote it at some length in his own words, as translated from the original Latin by his biographer, Leonhard Stejneger:

These animals love shallow and sandy places along the seashore, but they spend their time more particularly about the mouths of the gullies and brooks, the rushing fresh water of which always attracts them in herds. They keep the half-grown and young in front of them when pasturing, and are very careful to guard them in the rear and on the sides when travelling, always keeping them in the middle of the herd. With the rising tide they come in so close to the shore that not only did I on many occasions prod them with a pole or a spear, but sometimes even stroked their back with my hand. If badly hurt they did nothing more than move farther away from shore, but after a little while they forgot their injury and came back. Usually entire families keep together, the male with the female, one grown offspring and a little tender one. . . .

These gluttonous animals eat incessantly, and because of their enormous voracity keep their heads always under water with but slight concern for their life and security, so that one may pass in the very midst of them in a boat even unarmed and safely single out from the herd the one he wishes to hook. All they do while feeding is to lift the nostrils every four or five minutes out of the water, blowing out air and a little water with a noise like that of a horse snorting. While browsing they move slowly forward, one foot after the other, and in this manner half swim, half walk like cattle or sheep grazing. Half the body is always out of the water. Gulls are in the habit of sitting on the backs of the feeding animals feasting on the vermin infesting the skin, as crows are wont to do on the lice of hogs and sheep. . . . Where they have been staying even for a single day there may be seen immense heaps of roots and stems. Some of them when their bellies are full, go to sleep lying on their backs, first moving some distance away from the shore so as not to be left on dry land by the outgoing tide. . . .

In the spring they mate like human beings, particularly towards evening when the sea is calm. Before they come together many amorous preludes take place. The female, constantly followed by the male, swims leisurely to and fro eluding him with many gyrations and meanderings, until, impatient of further delay, she turns on her back as if exhausted and coerced, whereupon the male, rushing violently upon her, pays the tribute of his passion, and both give themselves over in mutual embrace.

Despite its vulnerability this charming and inoffensive animal was not at first molested by the ship-wrecked mariners. This can hardly be ascribed to any sentimental or compassionate feelings on their part, for to hungry stomachs in this bleak and forbidding wilderness the mountainous forms of *Rhytina* must have seemed a tempting prize indeed. The fact that they spared the animals for so long must, it seems, be put down to their feebleness, induced by scurvy, and to the fact that a readier source of food was available in the sea otters which could be procured in abundance by the simple formality of walking down to the beach with an improvised cudgel and banging them on the head. But as the men's health improved and the sea otters began to grow more wary, successful attempts were made to vary the menu with succulent steaks of sea-cow and sea-calf.

'Their capture was effected', wrote Steller, 'by a large iron hook, the point of which somewhat resembled the fluke of an anchor, the other end being fastened by means of an iron ring to a very long and stout rope, held by thirty men on shore. A strong sailor took this hook and with four or five other men stepped into the boat, and one of them taking the rudder, the other three or four rowing, they quietly hurried towards the herd. The harpooner stood in the bow of the boat with the hook in his hand and struck as soon as he was near enough to do so, whereupon the men on shore, grasping the other end of the rope, pulled the desperately resisting animal laboriously towards them. Those in the boat, however, made the animal fast by means of another rope and wore it out with continual blows, until, tired and completely motionless, it was attacked with bayonets, knives and other weapons and pulled up on land. Immense slices were cut from the still living animal, but all it did was to shake its tail furiously and make such resistance with its forelimbs that big strips of the cuticle were torn off. In addition it breathed heavily, as if sighing. From the wounds in the back the blood spurted upward like a fountain. As long as the head was under water no blood flowed, but as soon as it raised the head up to breathe the blood gushed forth anew.'

One final quotation from Steller tells how the herd used to try pathetically to help the struggling victim, and how the males gave touching proof of their devotion to their mates:

When an animal caught with the hook began to move about somewhat violently, those nearest in the herd began to stir also and feel the urge to bring succour. To this end some of them tried to upset the boat with their backs, while others pressed down the rope and endeavoured to break it, or strove to remove the hook from the wound in the back by blows of their tail, in which they actually succeeded several times. It is a most remarkable proof of their conjugal affection that the male, after having tried with all his might, although in vain, to free the female caught by the hook, and in spite of the beating we gave him, nevertheless followed her to the shore, and that several times, even after she was dead, he shot unexpectedly up to her like a speeding arrow. Early next morning, when we came to cut up the meat and bring it to the dugout, we found the male again standing by the female, and the same I observed once more on the third day when I went there by myself for the sole purpose of examing the intestines.

Despite the pathos of such accounts no one would dream of grudging these unhappy castaways the succulent steaks which were the reward of their efforts. They were in a desperate situation, and we must spare ourselves the sentimental indulgence of criticizing their apparent heartlessness. Their exploitation of *Rhytina* as a source of food only lasted for a few weeks before they sailed in the rebuilt *St. Peter* for the mainland, and can hardly be said to have played much part in its extermination. What is far less defensible is the series of events which followed during the next twenty-five years.

When the shipwrecked sailors returned to Kamchatka they brought with them the pelts of between eight and nine hundred sea otters, the remains of their eight months' meals. These were a very valuable commodity, and when word got round that both sea otters and blue foxes existed in profusion in the Commander Group the fur-hunters were not slow to take advantage of their opportunity. Copper Island and Bering Island became the headquarters of a flourishing eastern fur trade, and for those who like statistics it is recorded that in the next few years the slaughter carried out by only three hunters in the area amounted to over 11,000 foxes and 2,000 sea otters. The sea-cows themselves were not exploited to such a great extent for direct gain, for with the exception of their hides, which were anyway of limited value, they were of no commercial use. But the hunters and sailors who came in increasing numbers to the area required fresh meat, and owing to the excellent quality of sea-cow flesh and the comparative ease with which the animal could be caught, it was marked down at once as an easy source of food. Not surprisingly, the wholesale slaughter that ensued quickly brought the slow, dull-witted, but wholly inoffensive *Rhytina* to the verge of extinction.

The last of the sea-cows is often said to have been killed on Bering Island in 1786, only 27 years after the species' discovery. However, later in the nineteenth century Professor A. E. Nordenskiold collected evidence to show that it may have survived for rather longer than was originally thought. Apparently in 1780 sea-cows were still being killed as they fed on the seaweed, and their hides used for the making of skiffs. And two Russo-Aleutian creoles claimed to have seen on the coast of Bering Island as recently as 1834 a lean animal with a tapering body and small forelimbs, that blew through the mouth and had no back fins. As these observers were already familiar with fur seals, sea lions and walruses, and the other local animals which might otherwise have been regarded as responsible for the report, it seems at least possible that *Rhytina* existed in the area until just over a hundred years ago. In opposition to these arguments, however, many authorities believe that the animal seen by the creoles was a female narwhal, and that *Rhytina* itself was exterminated at a much earlier date.

During the period when the sea-cow was being done to death only one attempt was made to preserve it alive for posterity. This was initiated by a Russian mining engineer named Peter Jakovlev, who while prospecting in the Commander Group in 1755, found that the animal had already entirely disappeared from Copper Island. Unfortunately his petition for its protection elsewhere in the region – perhaps the earliest attempt at wild life conservation in the world's history – seems to have left the authorities in Kamchatka unmoved; anyway nothing was done to halt the progress of the animal's extermination.

Today the northern sea-cow – most lovable and fascinating of the great extinct animals of the recent past – can be studied only from a few dry bones and skeletons in museums, and from such rare original drawings as that reproduced earlier in this chapter from a contemporary chart of the *St. Peter's* voyage. The animal's discovery was due in the first place to man's perpetually questing spirit, which carried the early explorers into the most distant regions of the unknown world; its destruction to the obverse side of this same human spirit which always, it seems, must turn knowledge to material gain without counting the cost to the meek and lowly animals that share with us the tenancy of the Earth.

CHAPTER EIGHTEEN

Fossils of Tomorrow

And over them triumphant Death his Dart
Shook, but delaid to strike. . . .
                    MILTON: *Paradise Lost*

And, above all others, we should protect and hold sacred those
types, Nature's masterpieces, which are first singled out for destruction on account of their size, or splendour, or rarity, and that false
detestable glory which is accorded to their most successful slayers.
In ancient times the spirit of life shone brightest in these; and when
others that shared the earth with them were taken by death they
were left, being more worthy of perpetuation. Like immortal
flowers they have drifted down to us on the ocean of time, and their
strangeness and beauty bring to our imaginations a dream and a
picture of that unknown world, immeasurably far removed, where
man was not: and when they perish, something of gladness goes out
from nature, and the sunshine loses something of its brightness.

                    W. H. HUDSON: *The Naturalist in La Plata*

I N the last three chapters I have told how three absorbingly
interesting races of animals have been exterminated in comparatively recent times by the direct agency of man. This is
not to say that man was the sole cause of their extinction, for
every species is constantly exposed to a whole variety of external
influences to which it may or may not be sufficiently flexible to
adapt itself. But there can nevertheless be no doubt that the
additional strain imposed on the natural balance of things by
human persecution was the decisive factor in exterminating
these three species, as well as many others whose fate is equally
to be deplored.

Fortunately in the last fifty years there has been a gradual
change of heart in our attitude to the rarer animals that still
remain, and much more stringent measures are being taken
for their protection. Nearly every country now has an authorative body devoted to the study of fauna preservation, and such
related technical subjects as animal and plant ecology and
biological control. Big game hunters have taken to the camera
instead of the rifle, while even the fox-hunting fraternity are

finding that their enthusiasm for slaughter as a means of lessening the *ennui* of a winter's morning is no longer regarded with approbation, even by the unintelligent.

Yet despite this encouraging state of affairs several species of animals are still in imminent danger of extinction. In 1949 a Conference held at Lake Success by the Union Internationale pour la Protection de la Nature listed thirteen species of birds and fourteen species of mammals whose survival was severely threatened. The position after the 1954 Conference of the same organization held at Copenhagen showed some improvements but little fundamental change. A discussion of all the animals whose position and prospects were considered at these conferences would require a book in itself. I shall therefore have to restrict myself here to only two species whose lives are now literally hanging by a thread: the Javan rhinoceros and the strange New Zealand bird known as *Notornis*.

The Javan one-horned rhinoceros, *Rhinoceros sondaicus*, is now by far the rarest of the great land mammals of the Far East. It

A female Javan rhinoceros, *Rhinoceros sondaicus*

is smaller than the one-horned rhinoceros of India, *Rhinoceros unicornis*, and is additionally distinguished from it by the appearance of its skin. This looks cracked and scaly like that of a crocodile, and has a saddle-like fold in front of the shoulder, which passes right across the back. It stands about 5 feet

6 inches high and the single horn, which is normally only possessed by the male, measures less than a foot in length.

The animal was known to several early travellers, and its presence in Sumatra was specifically mentioned by William Marsden in 1811. But it was not officially listed as a distinct species until 1820, when two Frenchmen named Diard and Duvaucel sent a skeleton to the Musée d'Histoire Naturelle in Paris. Here it was examined and named by Baron Cuvier, and a description of its physical structure was published shortly afterwards by the French zoologist Anselme Desmarest. The animal had been discovered in Sumatra, which was then believed to be the full extent of its range, but otherwise no further information about it was available. Desmarest was forced to write in the section devoted to its habits the single word 'Unknown'.

But as time went on naturalists began to learn more facts about this interesting species of rhinoceros. Its range was found to be much greater than was originally supposed, and some reports showed it to exist not only in Sumatra, but in Java, Malaya, Burma, Siam, Assam, and possibly even in Borneo and French Indo-China. Until the 1870s or 1880s it was still common in the Sunderbans, the great delta of the Ganges, only a short distance from Calcutta. It seems to have been fairly adaptable in its choice of environment, but was more frequently met with in the thick evergreen forests of the plains than on high ground. It subsisted entirely on leaves, twigs, shoots, and other vegetable matter, and in the intervals of feeding spent much time wallowing contentedly in muddy pools, as rhinoceroses and elephants commonly do.

There are varying accounts of its character, some writers saying it was 'a quiet inoffensive beast', others that it was extremely savage and given to making unprovoked attacks on all and sundry. Duvaucel, the French zoologist who sent the first specimen to Paris, was attacked and seriously wounded by a one-horned rhinoceros in Bengal, while in 1827 a similar fate befell G. von Raalten, anatomist of the Natural History Committee of the Netherlands Indies at Krawang in Java. The rhinoceros first seized him with its mouth and then tossed him repeatedly with the horn, until he lay unconscious on the ground, As Mrs Heynius-Viruly dryly remarks in her survey of

East Indian fauna: 'They seem to have a special dislike for naturalists'.

During the nineteenth century the Javan rhinoceros began to go into decline. The story of its persecution for sport can be read in a dozen contemporary hunting books by senior officers serving in the Indian army, whose professional duties, devoted to the killing of their own species, apparently left ample time for the killing of others as well. Thus Colonel F. T. Pollock, in *Wild Sports of Burma and Assam* (1900), writes of the rhinoceros in Assam: 'I shot there forty-four to my own gun, and probably saw some sixty others slain, and lost wounded fully as many as I killed.' Even if we concede that this bag includes other species of rhinoceros than *sondaicus* the toll of destruction by this one hunter alone must have made no mean contribution to the animal's destruction.

But apart from the courageous white man with his elephants, beaters and battery of firearms, a heavy toll was taken by native hunters who killed the rhinoceros for gain. Throughout the Far East, and as far west as Arabia, rhinoceros horn is still supposed to have remarkable therapeutic properties. This is a survival from the days of zoological superstition which I discussed in the first part of this book, and is certainly due to the association of the rhinoceros with that most famous of legendary animals, the unicorn. Chinese pharmacies regard rhinoceros horn as an indispensable ingredient in concocting the many varieties of panaceas which they have made their speciality. Thus it is believed to be a sure remedy for snake-bite and an infallible means of detecting poison in a drink. Also, when powdered and swallowed with water it is said to have the most spectacular and attractive qualities as an aphrodisiac.

The price of such magic is naturally high, and quack doctors and chemists are prepared to pay large sums for the genuine article. Three thousand guilders, or about £350, is by no means an unusually high price for a single horn, and it is difficult to blame the native hunter for being tempted by such an inducement. Although the last thirty years have seen much legislation introduced to protect the Javan rhinoceros, poaching for the express purpose of obtaining the horn has undoubtedly done much to bring the animal to the verge of extinction.

What has been the position of the Javan rhinoceros during

the past two decades? Guy Dollman, writing in 1937, said that it was already so rare that an estimate of its numbers had to be based on individual specimens which had become well known. It was almost certainly extinct on the mainland of Asia except possibly for one or two specimens in Malaya. It might continue to flourish in Sumatra and there was a chance that it was still alive in western Java. Everywhere else it had been wiped out.

Today the position is even worse. The last Malayan specimens are almost certainly dead, which makes the animal extinct on the mainland. In Sumatra it is believed that there are now too few specimens left alive for the species to re-establish itself. Only in Java is there a glimmer of hope for the animal's future. Writing in *Oryx*, the Journal of the Fauna Preservation Society, in 1953 E. O. Shebbeare says: 'Today the Udjung Kolon sanctuary at the western extremity of Java is the main, probably the only, place where this species exists.' He reports that its numbers are estimated at 'not less than thirty nor more than fifty', and if poaching can, as at present, be prevented, there may be a chance that the numbers will increase. But a maximum of fifty lives, one must nevertheless feel, is a very slender life-line to preserve a species from annihilation.

Turning from the Javan rhinoceros to our second 'fossil of tomorrow', the New Zealand bird *Notornis*, we can for once comfort ourselves with the thought that man has played only an indirect part in its decline. It is now perhaps the most strictly and efficiently protected of all threatened animals, and every credit must go to the New Zealand Government for recognizing its scientific interest and taking prompt action to preserve it. But before discussing the present status of *Notornis* let us briefly recapitulate the interesting story of its past.

Notornis is a large bird of the rail family, looking like a moorhen but weighing as much as a goose, and when parts of its skeleton were first discovered in 1847, it was believed to be extinct. The bones were found on North Island by Walter Mantell, son of the famous Dr Gideon Mantell who, as related in an earlier chapter, discovered the dinosaur *Iguanodon*. They were in a sub-fossil condition, and were promptly forwarded to London, where they were described by Professor Owen and correctly identified as belonging to a previously unknown species of gallinule. This was duly named *Notornis mantelli* in honour of its discoverer, after which no one thought very much more about it.

Then a most surprising thing happened: the fossil *Notornis* came to life. In 1849 a party of sealers was camped on Resolution Island, near the south-west end of South Island, when one

Notornis, a fossil that came to life

of their number brought in a living example of the bird. Of course they had never heard of *Notornis* or even, we may suppose, of Professor Owen, and being practical men they promptly wrung the creature's neck and popped it in the pot. Nevertheless they must have been deeply impressed by its beautiful indigo blue and malachite green plumage, for they preserved the skin, which eventually, by a great stroke of luck, was acquired by Walter Mantell and despatched to London. Here Owen confirmed that this was indeed evidence of a living *Notornis*, and two years later a further capture by a party of Maoris in Thompson Sound, forty miles from Resolution Island, put the matter beyond any shadow of doubt.

Thereafter for 98 years only two specimens of *Notornis* came to the attention of naturalists. The first was killed by a dog, again in the same area near the south end of Lake Te Anau, and was acquired at an auction for £105 by the Dresden

Museum. The second was caught on the shore of Middle Fiord, Lake Te Anau in 1898, and in order to keep it in the country the New Zealand Government bought it for the high price of £250.

For the next half century no white man sighted a living *Notornis*. Despite intermittent reports from Maoris, who called the bird takahea (which ironically enough means 'wandering at large'), naturalists came to the sad conclusion that it had now finally disappeared. But there, in 1948, through the work of a New Zealand medical practitioner named G. B. Orbell, it was resurrected for the second time.

Since childhood Dr Orbell had been fascinated by the possibility that *Notornis* might still be alive. He made frequent visits from his home in Invercargill to the wild country west of Lake Te Anau where the earlier living birds had been discovered. In 1945 he built himself a summer residence there and was thus able to spend far more time in the area. Three years later his persistence was rewarded. He discovered a lake, previously unmarked on any map, which was nevertheless well known in Maori tradition as Kohaka-takahea, 'the nesting place of the wandering one'. And on the shore of the lake was the footprint of a bird.

Dr Orbell was convinced that this was the footprint of *Notornis*. He measured it by making notches on the stem of his pipe, and hurried back to civilization where he submitted a description of the footprint to Dr R. A. Falla of the Dominion Museum in Wellington, and a number of other experts. Their reaction was disappointing. Dr Falla thought it might possibly be a footprint of *Notornis*, but the other authorities were frankly sceptical. It was so much larger than the foot of the only New Zealand stuffed specimen that they felt it was more likely to belong to a bittern or a white heron.

Dr Orbell was undismayed by this damping verdict, and returned the following winter to his newly discovered lake. This time he was rewarded with sensational success. A few yards away from the site of the first print he saw new tracks that were so fresh that the sand still moved at their edges. And almost simultaneously he saw the bird itself. Nets were brought up and two specimens, a male and a female, were quickly caught. They were tethered on the lake shore where Dr Orbell made a coloured film of them as proof of his success. Then the birds were set free.

The rediscovery of *Notornis* caused a considerable stir in scientific circles, which was not surprising, and it also made front page news in the popular Press. Shortly afterwards the New Zealand Government made the whole region a reserve – not only the 500 acres which it was later found contained all the members of the Notornis colony, but a total area of 435,000 acres which, it was thought, would cover any other likely nesting sites in the vicinity. This was one of the most efficient and enlightened acts of any government in the field of fauna preservation in recent years.

Unfortunately, however, despite what has been done, *Notornis* may still become extinct within the next few decades. The first estimates of its number were later found to be too high. This was because they were based on a count of nests, and *Notornis* is a bird which often makes and abandons several nests before actually laying. It has also been suggested that the investigators themselves have unwittingly led to a reduction in the number of birds by disturbing them at their breeding sites. The most optimistic estimate of the surviving population is now about a hundred birds; several writers say forty, or even less. In any event the numbers are far too few for any optimistic view to be taken about the bird's survival.

Fortunately, as mentioned above, man has been the pre-server, and only indirectly the destroyer of *Notornis*. This indirect influence is seen in the deer and stoats found in the area, which are the bird's main enemies. (Deer have been known to walk on the nests, thus killing the chicks, while stoats, as is well known, are great eaters of eggs and young birds.) Both these animals were introduced into New Zealand by man, for formerly it was a country without land mammals of any kind. This is one more instance, like that of the introduction of the rabbit into Australia, which emphasizes the danger of interfering with the balance of nature without the most pain-staking study of the problems involved.

I have referred to the Javan rhinoceros and *Notornis* as 'fossils of tomorrow' because it would seem almost miraculous if they were to survive and re-establish themselves after their numbers have been so severely depleted. We must remember, however, that these are not the only creatures who today are in danger of following the quagga, the passenger pigeon and the great sea-cow to extinction. The banded anteater of Australia, and the Addo bush elephant and the bubal antelope of Africa; the Tasmanian marsupial wolf, and the strange little solenodon of Cuba; the ivory-billed woodpecker, the Hawaiian goose, and the North African ostrich; all these species and sub-species, as well as many others, are either extinct or very severely threatened. Surely we, who are at present the successful overlords of the Earth, must have enough wisdom, energy, and compassion to fight for the survivors and preserve them, if possible, to make their contribution to the wonder, the richness and the incredible diversity of life?

Bibliography

I. BEHIND THE LEGENDS

AELIANAS, CLAUDIUS. *De Natura Animalium*. Leipzig, 1864-6.

ALDROVANDI, ULISSE. *Serpentum et Draconum Historiae*. Bologna, 1640.

ALLEN, J. A. *History of North American Pinnipeds*. Washington, 1880.

ARISTOTLE. *Historia Animalium*. Trans. Richard Cresswell. London, 1862.

BALFOUR, EDWARD (Editor). *Cyclopaedia of India*, Second Supplement. Madras, 1862.

BARBOUR, T. 'Birth of a manatee.' *Journal of Mammalogy*, Vol. 18. Baltimore, 1937.

BARCLAY, JOHN. 'Remarks on some parts of the Animal that was cast ashore on the Island of Stronsa, September 1808.' *Memoirs of the Wernerian Natural History Society*, Vol. I. Edinburgh, 1811.

BARNUM, P. T. *The Life of P. T. Barnum, written by himself*. London, 1855.

BARRETT, O. W. 'Notes concerning manatees and dugongs.' *Journal of Mammalogy*, Vol. 16. Baltimore, 1935.

BARTON, MARGARET and Sir OSBERT SITWELL. *Sober Truth*. Duckworth, London, 1930.

BARTSCH, PAUL. 'Pirates of the Deep.' *Annual Report of the Smithsonian Institution* (1916). Washington, 1917.

BLAINVILLE, HENRI-MARIE DUCROTAY DE. 'Sur un nouveau genre de Serpent, *Scoliophis*, et le serpent de mer vu en Amerique en 1817.' *Journal de Physique, etc.*, Vol. 86. Paris, 1818.

BOBÉ, LOUIS. *Hans Egede, Colonizer and Missionary of Greenland*. Edited by Harold Ludlow. Copenhagen, 1952.

BOUYER, M. 'Poulpe géant observé entre Madère et Ténériffe.' *Comptes Rendus des Séances de l'Academie des Sciences*. Paris, 1861.

BROWNE, THOMAS, Sir. *Pseudodoxia Epidemica*. 2nd Edition, corrected and enlarged. London, 1650.

BUCKLAND, FRANCIS T. *Curiosities of Natural History*. 1st, 2nd, and New Series. London, 1858-66.

BULFINCH, THOMAS. *Bulfinch's Mythology*. Modern Library, New York, 1949.

BULLEN, F. T. *Creatures of the Sea*. London, 1904.

BYRNE, M. ST. CLARE. *The Elizabethan Zoo*. Etchells and MacDonald, London, 1926.

CARRINGTON, RICHARD. 'Edward Topsell and Elizabethan Natural History.' *Zoo Life*, Vol. 8. London, 1953.

CORY, ISAAC P. *Ancient Fragments of the Phoenician, . . . and other Writers*. London, 1832.

DARLING, F. FRASER. 'Seals of the World.' *Zoo Life*, Vol. 5. London, 1950.

DENNYS, N. B. *The Folk-Lore of China*. London, 1896.

EDWARDES, MARIAN and LEWIS SPENCE. *A Dictionary of Non-Classical Mythology*. Dent, London, 1912.

BIBLIOGRAPHY

EGEDE, HANS. *Det gamle Grønlands ny Perlustration* (1741). Edited by Louis Bobé. Copenhagen, 1925.

FIGUIER, LOUIS. *The Ocean World*. London, 1868.

FLACOURT, ETIENNE DE. *Histoire de la Grande Isle Madagascar*. 2nd Edition, enlarged. Paris, 1661.

GEOFFROY-SAINT-HILAIRE, ISIDORE. 'Notes sur des ossements et des œufs trouvés à Madagascar . . . provenant d'un Oiseau gigantesque.' *Comptes Rendus des Séances de l'Academie des Sciences*. Paris, 1851.

GESNER, CONRAD. *Historiae Animalium*. Zurich, 1551-87.

GIBSON, JOHN. *Monsters of the Sea*. London, 1887.

GIBSON-HILL, C. A. 'The Dugong.' *The Malayan Nature Journal*, Vol. 5. Kuala Lumpur, 1950.

GOLDSMID, EDMUND. *Un-natural History, or Myths of Ancient Science*. Translated from the works of Kirchmayer, Schookius, etc. Edinburgh, 1886.

GOSSE, PHILIP H. *The Romance of Natural History*, 1st and 2nd Series. London, 1860-1.

GOULD, CHARLES. *Mythical Monsters*. London, 1886.

GOULD, RUPERT T. *The Case for the Sea Serpent*. Allan, London, 1930.

GOULD, RUPERT T. *The Loch Ness Monster and Others*. Bles, London, 1934.

GOULD, S. BARING. *Curious Myths of the Middle Ages*. New and enlarged edition. London, 1869.

GRANDIDIER, ALFRED. *Histoire de la Géographie de Madagascar*. Paris, 1885-92.

GRAVES, ROBERT. *The White Goddess*. Faber, London, 1952.

GUBERNATIS, ANGELO DE, Count. *Zoological Mythology*. London, 1872.

HAMILTON, ROBERT. *The Natural History of Amphibious Carnivora*, etc. The Naturalist's Library, Vol. 6. London, 1843.

HERODOTUS. *The Histories*. Translated by Henry Cary. London, 1901.

HOME, EVERARD, Sir. 'An anatomical account of *Squalus maximus*.' *Philosophical Transactions of the Royal Society*, Vol. 99. London, 1809.

HUDSON, HENRY and others. 'Divers Voyages and Northern Discoveries of Henry Hudson.' From *Purchas his Pilgrimes*. London, 1625.

HULME, F. E. *Natural History Lore and Legend*. London, 1895.

JONES, J. A. *Tales of an Indian Camp*. London, 1829.

LAMBRECHT, KÁLMAN. *Handbuch der Palaeornithologie*. Berlin, 1933.

LANE, E. W. (translator). *The Arabian Nights' Entertainments*. Edited by S. Lane-Poole. Bell, London, 1925.

LEACH, MARIA (Editor). *Funk and Wagnall's Standard Dictionary of Folklore, Mythology and Legend*. New York, 1950.

LEE, HENRY. *Sea Fables Explained*. London, 1884.

LEE, HENRY. *Sea Monsters Unmasked*. London, 1884.

LEE, HENRY. *The Octopus*. London, 1875.

LINNAEAN SOCIETY OF NEW ENGLAND. *Report . . . relative to a large marine animal . . . seen near Cape Ann, Massachusetts in August 1817*. Boston, 1817.

LITTLE, H. W. *Madagascar: Its History and People*. London, 1884.

LOCKHART, J. G. *Mysteries of the Sea*. Allan, London, 1928.

LUCIAN of Samosata. *Works*. Translated by H. W. and F. G. Fowler. Oxford, 1905.

LUM, PETER. *Fabulous Beasts*. Thames and Hudson, London, 1952.

BIBLIOGRAPHY

MACKENZIE, DONALD A. *Indian Myth and Legend.* London, 1913.

MACKWORTH-PRAED, C. W. and C. H. B. GRANT. *Birds of Eastern and North Eastern Africa.* Longmans, Green and Co., London, New York and Toronto, 1952.

MAGNUS OLAUS. *Historia de Gentibus Septentrionalibus.* Antwerp, 1558.

MAGNUS, OLAUS. *A Compendious History of the Goths, etc.* (A translation of the *Historia de Gentibus Septentrionalibus.*) London, 1658.

MANTELL, GIDEON A. The Fossil Sea Serpent. *Illustrated London News.* London, 4 Nov. 1848.

MEADE-WALDO, E. G. B. and MICHAEL J. NICOLL. 'Description of an unknown Animal seen at sea off the coast of Brazil.' *Proceedings of the Zoological Society of London.* 1906.

MEINERTZHAGEN, R. *Nicoll's Birds of Egypt.* Rees, London, 1930.

MILNE-EDWARDS, ALPHONSE. *Oiseaux Fossiles de la France.* Paris, 1867-71.

MINER, ROY WALDO. 'Marauders of the Sea.' *The National Geographic Magazine,* Vol. 68. Washington, 1935.

MONTFORT, PIERRE DENIS DE. 'Histoire Naturelle Générale et Particuliére des Mollusques.' From Sonnini's expanded edition of Buffon's *Natural History.* Paris, 1802-5.

MOOK, CHARLES C. 'The Ancestry of the Alligators.' *Natural History,* Vol. 25. American Museum of Natural History, New York, 1925.

MOORE, J. C. 'The status of the manatee in the Everglades National Park, etc.' *Journal of Mammalogy,* Vol. 32. Baltimore, 1951.

MOQUIN-TANDON, M. 'Note sur un Céphalopode ou poulpe monstrueux.' *Comptes Rendus des Séances de l'Academie des Sciences.* Paris, 1861.

MORUS (i.e. RICHARD LEWINSOHN). *Animals, Men and Myths.* Gollancz, London, 1954.

M'QUHAE, PETER and others. 'The Daedalus Sea Serpent.' *Illustrated London News.* London, 28 Oct. 1849.

MURRAY, JOHN, Sir, and JOHAN HJORT. *The Depths of the Ocean.* London, 1912.

NICOLL, MICHAEL J. *Three Voyages of a Naturalist.* London, 1908.

NORMAN, J. R. and F. C. FRASER. *Giant Fishes, Whales and Dolphins.* Putnam, London, 1937.

OGILBY, JOHN. *Africa.* (An expanded version of the book of the same name by Olfert Dapper.) London, 1670.

OLIVER, S. P. *Madagascar.* London, 1886.

OUDEMANS, A. C. *The Great Sea Serpent.* Leiden, 1892.

OWEN, RICHARD, Sir. Letter on the Daedalus Sea Serpent. *The Times.* London, 14 Nov. 1848.

PACKARD, A. S. 'Colossal Cuttle Fishes.' *American Naturalist,* Vol. 7. Salem, Massachusetts, 1873.

PLINY (Caius Plinius Secundus). *The Historie of the World.* The first English translation, by Philemon Holland, of Pliny's *Natural History.* London, 1601.

POLO, MARCO. *The Travels of Marco Polo.* Translated and edited by Sir Henry Yule. Murray, London, 1921.

PONTOPPIDAN, ERIK. *Natural History of Norway.* London, 1755.

POPE, CLIFFORD H. *The Reptiles of China*. American Museum of Natural History, New York, 1935.

RENARD, LOUIS (Publisher). *Poissons Ecrevisses et Crabes . . . des Isles Moluques, etc.* Pictures by S. Fallours. Amsterdam, 1718.

ROBINSON, PHIL. *Fishes of Fancy*. London, 1884.

ROGERS, H. D. 'Remarks upon the bones of the Zeuglodon, recently exhibited in Boston . . . by their proprietor, Dr Koch.' *Proceedings of the Boston Society of Natural History*, Vol. 2. 1845. Boston, 1848.

RONDELETIUS, GULIELMUS. *Libri de Piscibus Marinis*. Lyon, 1554-5.

SALIM ALI. *The Book of Indian Birds*. Bombay Natural History Society, 1946.

SIBREE, JAMES. *The Great African Island*. London, 1880.

SIBREE, JAMES. *A Naturalist in Madagascar*. London, 1915.

SIEBOLD, P. F. VON. *Manners and Customs of the Japanese in the nineteenth century*. London, 1841.

SMITH, WILLIAM, Sir. *Dictionary of Greek and Roman Biography and Mythology*. London, 1844-9.

SOWERBY, ARTHUR DE CARLE. *China's Natural History*. Royal Asiatic Society, Shanghai, 1936.

SOWERBY, ARTHUR DE CARLE. *A Naturalist's Note-Book in China*. Shanghai, 1925.

STEINMETZ, ANDREW. *Japan and Her People*. London, 1859.

SWANN, H. KIRKE. *A Monograph of the Birds of Prey*. Wheldon and Wesley, London, 1924-45.

TENNENT, J. EMERSON, Sir. *Sketches of the Natural History of Ceylon*. London, 1861.

TOPSELL, EDWARD. *The Historie of Foure-Footed Beastes*. London, 1607.

TOPSELL, EDWARD. *The Historie of Serpents*. London, 1608.

VALENTIJN, FRANÇOIS. *Oud en Nieuw Oost-Indien, etc.* Dordrecht and Amsterdam, 1724-6.

VALERIUS MAXIMUS. *Valerii Maximi dictorum et factorum memorabilium*. Venice, 1502.

VERRILL, A. E. 'The Colossal Cephalopods of the Western Atlantic.' *American Naturalist*, Vol. 9. Salem, Massachusetts, 1875.

VINYCOMB, JOHN. *Fictitious and Symbolic Creatures in Art*. London, 1906.

WALDRON, GEORGE. *The History and Description of the Isle of Man, etc.* London, 1744.

WERNER, E. T. CHALMERS. *Myths and Legends of China*. Harrap, London, 1922.

WIEDEMANN, ALFRED. 'Die Phönix-Sage im alten Aegypten.' *Zeitschrift für ägyptische Sprache und Alterthumskunde.*, Vol. 16. Leipzig, 1878.

WHISTLER, HUGH. *Popular Handbook of Indian Birds*. 4th Edition revised and enlarged by Sir Norman Kinnear. Gurney and Jackson. London, 1949.

WHITBOURNE, RICHARD. *A Discourse and Discovery of New-found-land*. London, 1622.

WRAXALL, LASCELLES, Sir. *Life in the Sea*. London, 1860.

WYMAN, JEFFRIES. 'Observations on fossil bones of *Zeuglodon*.' *Proceedings of the Boston Society of Natural History*, Vol. 3, 1850. Cambridge, New England, 1851.

BIBLIOGRAPHY

WYMAN, JEFFRIES. 'The fossil skeleton recently exhibited in New York as that of a sea-serpent, etc.' *Proceedings of the Boston Society of Natural History*, Vol. 2, 1845. Boston, 1848.

II. STONE TESTAMENT

ALLBUTT, THOMAS CLIFFORD, Sir. *Palissy, Bacon, and the Revival of Natural Science*. London, 1914.

ANDREWS, CHARLES WILLIAM. *A Descriptive Catalogue of the Tertiary Vertebrata of the Fayûm, Egypt*. British Museum (Natural History), London, 1906.

ASHE, T. *Memoirs of Mammoth and various other extraordinary and stupendous Bones of incognita, or non-descript animals, etc.* Liverpool, 1806.

BEADNELL, H. J. L. *The Topography and Geology of the Fayûm Province of Egypt*. Survey Department, Cairo, 1905.

BERINGER, JOHANNES BARTHOLOMEW. *Lithographica Würceburgensis*. Würzburg, 1726.

BUCKLAND, WILLIAM. 'Notice on the *Megalosaurus*, or great Fossil Lizard of Stonesfield.' *Transactions of the Geological Society of London*, Series 2, Vol. 1. London, 1824.

BUFFON, GEORGES LOUIS LE CLERC, Comte de. *Époques de la Nature*. Paris, 1778.

CARRINGTON, RICHARD. *A Guide to Earth History*. Chatto and Windus, London, 1956.

CASTERET, NORBERT. *Ten Years Under the Earth*. Penguin Books, London 1952.

CLEMENS, SAMUEL LANGHORNE ('MARK TWAIN'). 'Carson Footprints.' *Daily Record-Union*, Sacramento, 25 March 1885.

COLBERT, E. H. *The Dinosaur Book*. McGraw-Hill, New York, 1951.

COPE, EDWARD DRINKER. 'The Vertebrata of the Cretaceous Formations of the West.' *Report of the U.S. Geological Survey of the Territories*, Vol. 2. Washington, 1875.

CUVIER, GEORGES LÉOPOLD CHRÉTIEN FRÉDÉRIC DAGOBERT, Baron. *Récherches sur les Ossemens Fossiles*. Paris, 1812.

DARWIN, CHARLES. *Journal of Researches into the Natural History and Geology of the Countries Visited during the Voyage of H.M.S. Beagle Round the World*. London, 1842.

DEANE, JAMES. 'Fossil Footprints of the Connecticut River.' *Journal of the Academy of Natural Sciences of Philadelphia*, Series 2, Vol. 2. Philadelphia, 1850-4.

DEANE, JAMES. 'On the Sandstone Fossils of Connecticut River. *Journal of the Academy of Natural Sciences of Philadelphia*, Series 2, Vol. 3. Philadelphia, 1855-8.

DIGBY, BASSETT. *The Mammoth and Mammoth Hunting in North East Siberia*. Witherby, London, 1926.

DOLLO, LOUIS. 'Les Découvertes de Bernissart.' *Annales des Sciences Géologiques*, Vol. 16. Paris, 1884.

BIBLIOGRAPHY

DOLLO, LOUIS. 'Notes sur les Dinosauriens de Bernissart' (5 papers). *Bulletin du Musée Royal d'Histoire Naturelle de Belgique*, Vols. 1, 2 and 3. Brussels, 1882-4.

DUPONT, E. 'Sur la découverte d'ossements d'Iguanodons, de Poissons et végétaux dans la fosse Sainte-Barbe du charbonnage de Bernissart.' *Bulletin de l'Académie Royale de Belgique*, Series 2, Vol. 46. Brussels, 1878.

EGERTON, PHILIP GREY, Sir. 'On Two Casts in Sandstone of the Impressions of the Hind foot of a Gigantic *Cheirotherium*, from the New Red Sandstone of Cheshire.' *Proceedings of the Geological Society of London*, Vol. 3. London, 1838-40.

FOULKE, WILLIAM PARKER. 'Statement respecting fossil bones found at Haddonfield, Camden County, New Jersey.' *Proceedings of the Academy of Natural Sciences of Philadelphia*, 1858. Philadelphia, 1859.

HABICOT, NICOLAS. *Antigigantologie*. Paris, 1618.

HABICOT, NICOLAS. *Gygantosteologie, ou Discours des os d'un Géant*. Paris, 1613.

HARKNESS, ROBERT. 'On Fossil Footprints.' *Edinburgh New Philosophical Journal*, Vol. 52. Edinburgh, 1852.

HERTZ, O. F. 'Frozen Mammoth in Siberia.' *Annual Report of the Smithsonian Institution*, 1903. Washington, 1904.

HITCHCOCK, EDWARD. 'Report on Ichnolithology, or Fossil Footmarks, etc.' *American Journal of Science*, Series 1, Vol. 47. New Haven, 1844.

HOOLEY, REGINALD WALTER. 'On the Skeleton of *Iguanodon atherfieldensis*, sp. nov., from the Wealden Shales of Atherfield (Isle of Wight).' *Quarterly Journal of the Geological Society of London*, Vol. 81. London, 1925.

HOWORTH, HENRY H. *The Mammoth and the Flood*. London, 1887.

HOWORTH, HENRY H. 'The Mammoth in Siberia.' *Geological Magazine*, Vol. 7. London, 1880.

HOWORTH, HENRY H. 'The Sudden Extinction of the Mammoth.' *Geological Magazine*, Vol. 8. London, 1881.

HUTCHINSON, H. N. *Extinct Monsters*. London, 1897.

HUTTON, JAMES. *The Theory of the Earth*. Edinburgh, 1785.

IDES, YSBRANTS EVERT. *Three Years Travels from Moscow over-land to China*. London, 1706.

KIRCHER, ATHANASIUS. *Mundas subterraneus, etc.* Amsterdam, 1665.

LAMARCK, JEAN BAPTISTE PIERRE ANTOINE DE MONET, Chevalier de. *Philosophie Zoologique*. Paris, 1809.

LANG, HERBERT. 'Problems and Facts about Frozen Siberian Mammoths (*Elephas primigenius*) and their Ivory.' *Zoologica*, Vol. 4. New York, 1925.

LANKESTER, E. RAY, Sir. *Extinct Animals*. London, 1906.

LE CONTE, JOSEPH. 'Carson Footprints.' *Nature*, Vol. 28. London, 1883.

LEIDY, JOSEPH. 'Contributions to the Extinct Vertebrate Fauna of the Western Territories.' *Report of the U.S. Geological Survey of the Territories*, Vol. 1. Washington, 1873.

LEIDY, JOSEPH. *Cretaceous Reptiles of the United States*. Philadelphia, 1865.

LEY, WILLY. *Dragons in Amber*. Sidgwick and Jackson, London, 1951.

LULL, R. S. *Fossils*. University Society, New York, 1931.

LULL, R. S. *Triassic Life of the Connecticut Valley*. Hartford, 1915.

LYELL, CHARLES, Sir. *A Manual of Elementary Geology* (3rd Edition). London, 1851.

LYELL, CHARLES, Sir. *Principles of Geology*. London, 1830-3.

LYELL, CHARLES, Sir. *Travels in North America*, 1841-2. New York, 1845.

MACK, EFFIE MONA. *Mark Twain in Nevada*. Charles Scribner's Sons, New York, 1947.

MANTELL, GIDEON A. 'Notice on the *Iguanodon*, a newly discovered fossil reptile from the sandstone of Tilgate Forest, in Sussex.' *Philosophical Transactions of the Royal Society*, Vol. 115. London, 1825.

MANTELL, GIDEON A. 'On the Structure of the *Iguanodon*, and on the Fauna and Flora of the Wealden Formation.' *Edinburgh New Philosophical Journal*, Vol. 53. Edinburgh, 1852.

MANTELL, GIDEON A. *Wonders of Geology*. London, 1838.

MARSH, OTHNIEL CHARLES. 'The Dinosaurs of North America.' *16th Annual Report of the U.S. Geological Survey*. Washington, 1896.

MARSH, OTHNIEL CHARLES. 'On the Supposed Human Foot-prints recently found in Nevada.' *American Journal of Science*, Series 3, Vol. 26. New Haven, 1883.

MATHER, COTTON. 'An Account of several Observations made in New England in 1712.' *Philosophical Transactions of the Royal Society*, Vol. 29. London, 1714.

NEUVILLE, H. 'On the Extinction of the Mammoth.' *Annual Report of the Smithsonian Institution*, 1919. Washington, 1921.

NEVADA. *A Guide to the Silver State*. Portland, Oregon, 1940.

OSBORN, HENRY FAIRFIELD. *Proboscidea*. American Museum of Natural History, New York, 1936-42.

OWEN, RICHARD, Sir. *A History of British Fossil Reptiles*. London, 1849-84.

OWEN, RICHARD, SIR. *Palaeontology* (2nd Edition). Edinburgh, 1861.

OWEN, RICHARD, Sir. 'Report on British Fossil Reptiles, Part 2.' *Report of the Eleventh Meeting of the British Association for the Advancement of Science*. (Plymouth, 1841.) London, 1842.

OWEN, RICHARD, Sir. 'Report on the *Missourium* now exhibiting at the Egyptian Hall, etc.' *Proceedings of the Geological Society of London*, Vol. 3. London, 1838-42.

PEABODY, FRANK E. 'Reptile and Amphibian Trackways from the Lower Triassic Moenkopi Formation of Arizona and Utah.' *Bulletin of the Department of Geological Sciences*, Vol. 27. University of California Press, Berkeley and Los Angeles, 1948.

PFIZENMAYER, E. W. *Mammutleichen und Urwaldmenschen in Nordost-Sibirien*. Leipzig, 1926.

REEDS, CHESTER A. (Editor). 'The Romance of Fossil Hunting.' *Natural History*, Vol. 26, No. 5. American Museum of Natural History, New York, 1926.

RIOLAN, JEAN, the Younger. *Gigantologie*. Paris, 1618.

RIOLAN, JEAN, the Younger. *Gigantomachie*. Paris, 1613.

RIOLAN, JEAN, the Younger. *L'Imposture descouverte des os humains supposés et faussement attribués au roy Theutobochus*. Paris, 1614.

BIBLIOGRAPHY

SCHUCHERT, CHARLES and CLARA MAY LEVENE. *O. C. Marsh, Pioneer in Palaeontology.* Yale University Press, New Haven, 1940.

SIMPSON, GEORGE GAYLORD. *Life of the Past.* Yale University Press, New Haven, 1953.

SMITH, NATHAN. 'Fossil Bones found in red sand stone.' *American Journal of Science,* Series 1, Vol. 2. New Haven, 1820.

SOERGEL, WOLFGANG. *Die Fährten der Chirotheria.* Fischer, Jena, 1925.

SPOKES, SIDNEY. *Gideon Algernon Mantell, Surgeon and Geologist.* London, 1927.

STENO, NICOLAUS. *De solido intra solidum naturaliter contento.* Florence, 1669.

STERNBERG, CHARLES H. *Hunting Dinosaurs.* Lawrence, Kansas, 1917.

STERNBERG, CHARLES H. *The Life of a Fossil Hunter.* New York, 1909.

SWINTON, W. E. *The Dinosaurs.* Murby, London, 1934.

SWINTON, W. E. *Fossil Amphibians and Reptiles.* British Museum (Natural History), London, 1954.

SWINTON, W. E. 'A New Exhibit of *Iguanadon.*' *Natural History Magazine,* Vol. 4. London, 1933.

TOLMACHOFF, I. P. 'The Carcasses of the Mammoth and Rhinoceros found in the frozen ground of Siberia.' *Transactions of the American Philosophical Society,* Vol. 23. Philadelphia, 1933.

TUKEMAN, HENRY. 'The Killing of the Mammoth.' *McClure's Magazine,* October, 1899. The S. S. McClure Co., New York and London, 1899.

TWAIN, MARK. See CLEMENS, SAMUEL LANGHORNE.

WARREN, JOHN C. *Description of a Skeleton of the Mastodon Giganteus of North America.* Boston, 1852.

WATSON, D. M. S. 'The Cheirotherium.' *Geological Magazine,* Series 6, Vol. 1. London, 1914.

ZITTEL, C. A. VON. *History of Geology and Palaeontology.* London, 1901.

ZITTEL, C. A. VON. *Text-book of Palaeontology,* Vol. 2. (Revised by Sir Arthur Smith Woodward.) Macmillan, London, 1932.

III. LIVING LINKS WITH THE PAST

ANDREWS, HENRY N. *Ancient Plants and the World They Lived in.* Comstock, New York, 1947.

ARNOLD, CHESTER A. *An Introduction to Paleobotany.* McGraw-Hill, New York, 1947.

BARRETT, CHARLES. *The Platypus.* Robertson and Mullens, Melbourne, 1944.

BELT, THOMAS. *The Naturalist in Nicaragua.* London, 1874.

BOUVIER, E. L. 'Monographie des Onychophores.' *Annales des Sciences Naturelles,* Series 9, Vol. 2. and Vol. 5. Paris, 1905.

BUCHSBAUM, RALPH. *Animals without Backbones.* University of Chicago Press, Chicago, 1948.

BURRELL, HARRY. *The Platypus.* Angus and Robertson, Sydney, 1927.

BURTON, MAURICE. *Living Fossils.* Thames and Hudson, London and New York, 1954.

CALVERT, ALBERT F. *The Discovery of Australia.* 2nd Edition, revised and enlarged. London, 1902.

BIBLIOGRAPHY

COLBERT, E. H. 'A Fossil Comes to Life.' *Natural History*, Vol. 43. American Museum of Natural History, New York, 1939.

COOK, JAMES. *Captain Cook's Journal during his First Voyage Round the World made in H.M. Bark 'Endeavour'*. 1768-71. Edited by Captain W. J. L. Wharton. London, 1895.

DAMPIER, WILLIAM. *A Collection of Voyages*. London, 1729.

DECHASEAUX, COLETTE. 'Onychophores.' (From: *Traité de Paléontologie*, by Jean Piveteau, Vol. 3.) Masson, Paris, 1953.

DU TOIT, ALEX. L. *Our Wandering Continents*. Oliver and Boyd, Edinburgh and London, 1937.

DU TOIT, Alex. L. 'Tertiary Mammals and Continental Drift.' *American Journal of Science*, Vol. 242. New Haven, 1944.

EADIE, ROBERT. *The Life and Habits of the Platypus*. Stillwell and Stephens, Melbourne, 1935.

EDEN, RICHARD. *The History of Travayle in the West and East Indies, etc.* London, 1577.

FLEAY, DAVID. *We Breed the Platypus*. Robertson and Mullens, Melbourne, 1944.

GREGORY, WILLIAM K. 'Australia, the Land of Living Fossils.' *Natural History*, Vol. 24. American Museum of Natural History, New York, 1924.

GREGORY, WILLIAM K. *Our Face from Fish to Man*. Putnam, New York and London, 1929.

GUILDING, LANDSDOWN. 'An Account of a New Genus of Mollusca.' *Zoological Journal*, Vol. 2. 1825-1826. London, 1826.

HARRISON, LAUNCELOT. 'The composition and origins of the Australian fauna, with special reference to the Wegener hypothesis.' *Report of the Australasian Association for the Advancement of Science*, Vol. 18. Perth, 1928.

HARTMAN, CARL G. *Possums*. University of Texas Press, 1952.

HAWKESWORTH, JOHN. *An Account of the Voyages undertaken by the order of His Present Majesty for making Discoveries in the Southern Hemisphere*, Vol. 3. London, 1773.

HOME, EVARARD, Sir. 'A Description of the Anatomy of the *Ornithorhynchus paradoxus*.' *Philosophical Transactions of the Royal Society*, London, 1802.

HUTCHINSON, G. E. 'Restudy of some Burgess shale fossils.' *Proceedings of the United States National Museum*, Vol. 78, 1930. Washington, 1931.

HUXLEY, THOMAS HENRY. 'Illustrations of the Structure of the Crossopterygian Ganoids.' (From: Figures and Descriptions illustrative of British Organic Remains, Decade 12.) *Memoirs of the Geological Survey of the United Kingdom*, London, 1866.

JONES, F. WOOD. *The Mammals of South Australia*. (Part 1: Monotremes and Carnivorous Marsupials.) Adelaide, 1923.

KAEMPFER, ENGELBERT. *Amoenitatum exoticarum, etc.* Lemgo, Germany, 1712.

KAEMPFER, ENGELBERT. *The History of Japan ... together with a description of the Kingdom of Siam.* Translated by J. G. Scheuchzer. London, 1727.

KNOX, ROBERT. 'On the Anatomy of the *Ornithorhynchus Paradoxus* of New South Wales.' *Edinburgh Philosophical Journal*, Vol. 9. Edinburgh, 1823.

BIBLIOGRAPHY

LE SOUEF, A. S. and HARRY BURRELL. *The Wild Animals of Australasia.* Harrap, London, 1926.

LEY, WILLY. *The Lungfish and the Unicorn.* Hutchinson, London, 1948.

LORUS, J. and MARGERY J. MILNE. 'The Worm that didn't turn into anything.' *Natural History*, Vol. 63. American Museum of Natural History, New York, 1954.

LOUDON, JOHN CLAUDIUS. *Arboretum et Fruticetum Britannicum*, Vol. 4. London, 1838.

MANTON, S. M. 'The Evolution of the Arthropodan Locomotory Mechanisms.' (Part 1: The Locomotion of Peripatus, 1949.) *Journal of the Linnaean Society of London*, Vol. 41. London, 1940-50.

MILLOT, J. H. 'Le Continent de Gondwana et les méthodes de raisonnement de la bio-géographie classique.' *Annales des Sciences Naturelles*, Series 11, Zoologie et Biologie Animale, Vol. 15. Masson, Paris, 1953.

MILLOT, J. H. 'Further Study of the Coelacanth.' *The Times*, London, 3 June 1954.

MILLOT, J. H. 'Le Troisième Coelacanthe.' *Naturaliste Malgache*, Supplement No. 1. Tananarive-Tsimbazaza, 1954.

NORMAN, J. R. 'A Living Coelacanth from South Africa.' *Proceedings of the Linnaean Society*, 1938-1939. London, 1939-41.

ROGERS, J. D. *A Historical Geography of the British Colonies*, Vol. 6. Oxford, 1907.

SCHAEFFER, BOBB. 'The Triassic Coelacanth Fish *Diplurus* with Observations on the Evolution of the Coelacanthini.' *Bulletin of the American Museum of Natural History*. Vol. 99. New York, 1952.

SCOTT, ERNEST. *Australian Discovery.* Dent, London and Toronto, 1929.

SEDGWICK, ADAM. 'A Monograph on the Species and Distribution of the genus *Peripatus*.' *Quarterly Journal of Microscopical Science*, New Series, Vol. 28. London, 1888.

SEWARD, ALGERNON CHARLES, Sir. *Fossil Plants*, Vol. 4. Cambridge University Press, 1919.

SEWARD, ALGERNON CHARLES, Sir. *Links with the Past in the plant World.* Cambridge University Press, 1911.

SEWARD, ALGERNON CHARLES, Sir. *Plant Life Through the Ages.* Cambridge University Press, 1947.

SEWARD, ALGERNON CHARLES, Sir. 'The Story of the Maidenhair Tree.' *Science Progress*, Vol. 32, No. 127. London, 1938.

SHAW, GEORGE. 'The Duck-billed Platypus.' *Naturalist's Miscellany*, Vol. 10. London, 1799.

SIMPSON, GEORGE GAYLORD. 'Mammals and the Nature of Continents.' *American Journals of Science*, Vol. 241. New Haven, 1943.

SMITH, J. L. B. 'A Living Coelacanthid Fish from South Africa.' *Transactions of the Royal Society of South Africa*, Vol. 28. Cape Town, 1941.

SMITH, J. L. B. *The Sea Fishes of Southern Africa.* Central News Agency, South Africa, 1950.

SMITH, J. L. B. 'The Second Coelacanth.' *Nature*, Vol. 171. London, 1953.

SMITH, J. L. B. 'A Surviving Fish of the Order Actinistia.' *Transactions of the Royal Society of South Africa*, Vol. 27. Cape Town, 1940.

BIBLIOGRAPHY

SYMPOSIUM ON THE THEORY OF CONTINENTAL DRIFT. *Advancement of Science*, Vol. 8, No. 29. British Association for the Advancement of Science, London, 1951.

SYMPOSIUM ON THE THEORY OF CONTINENTAL DRIFT. American Association of Petroleum Geologists, Tulsa, Oklahoma, 1928.

TERMIER, PIERRE. 'La Dérive des Continents.' *Bulletin de I'Institut Océanographique*, No. 443. Musée Océanographique, Monaco, 1924.

WALCOTT, C. D. 'Middle Cambrian Annelids.' *Smithsonian Miscellaneous Collection*, Vol. 57. Washington, 1914.

WALLACE, ALFRED RUSSELL. *The Geographical Distribution of Animals.* London, 1876.

WATSON, D. M. S. 'Coelacanths.' *New Biology*, No. 16. Penguin Books, London, 1954.

WEGENER, ALFRED LOTHAR. *The Origin of Continents and Oceans.* Translated by J. G. A. Skerl. Methuen, London, 1924.

WHITE, E. I. 'The Coelacanth Fishes.' *Discovery*, Vol. 14, No. 4. London, 1953.

WHITE, E. I. 'More About the Coelacanths.' *Discovery*, Vol. 15, No. 8. London, 1954.

WOODWARD, ARTHUR SMITH, Sir. 'The Surviving Crossopterygian Fish *Latimeria*.' *Nature*, Vol. 146. London, 1940.

IV. THE DEATH OF RACES

ABBOTT, ROY L. 'The Passing of the Passenger Pigeon.' *Natural History*, Vol. 53. American Museum of Natural History, New York, 1944.

ALLEN, GLOVER M. *Extinct and Vanishing Mammals of the Western Hemisphere.* ✓ American Committee for International Wild Life Protection, New York, 1942.

AUDUBON, JOHN JAMES. *Birds of America.* New York, 1839.

BENDIRE, CHARLES. *Life Histories of North American Birds.* Washington, 1892.

BRYDEN, H. A. (Editor). *Great and Small Game of Africa.* London, 1899.

BUFFON, GEORGE LOUIS LECLERC, Comte de. *Histoire Naturelle: Quadrupèdes*, Vol. 8. Paris, 1787.

BURCHELL, WILLIAM J. *Travels in the Interior of Southern Africa.* London, 1899.

CATESBY, MARK. *The Natural History of Carolina, Florida, and the Bahama Islands.* London, 1731.

CUMMING, R. GORDON. *Five Years of a Hunter's life in the Far Interior of South Africa.* London, 1850.

CUVIER, GEORGES LÉOPOLD CHRÉTIEN FRÉDÉRIC DAGOBERT, Baron. *The Animal Kingdom, arranged in conformity with its Organization; with additional descriptions of all Species hitherto named, and of many not before noticed, by Edward Griffith, S. H. Smith, E. Pidgeon, etc.* London, 1827-34.

DESMAREST, ANSELME GAËTAN. *Mammalogie.* Paris, 1820-22.

DOLLMAN, GUY. 'Mammals which have recently become extinct and those on the verge of extinction.' *Journal of the Society for the Preservation of the Fauna of the Empire*, New Series, No. 30. Hertford, 1937.

EDWARDS, GEORGE. *Gleanings of Natural History*. London, 1758.

FALLA, R. A. 'Notornis Re-discovered.' *Emu*, Vol. 48. Melbourne, 1949.

FLOWER, STANLEY SMYTH. 'On the Mammalia of Siam and the Malay Peninsula.' *Proceedings of the Zoological Society of London*, 1900.

FREUND, L. 'A Bibliography of the Mammalian Order Sirenia.' *Věstník Československé Zoologické Společnosti*, Vol. 14. Prague, 1950.

GOLDER, F. A. *Bering's Voyages*. American Geographical Society, New York, 1922-5.

GOODWIN, GEORGE C. 'The End of the Great Northern Sea Cow.' *Natural History*, Vol. 55. American Museum of Natural History, New York, 1946.

HAHN, C. H. 'A Quagga Inquiry.' *Journal of the Society for the Preservation of the Fauna of the Empire*, New Series, No. 39. Hertford, 1940.

HARPER, FRANCIS. *Extinct and Vanishing Mammals of the Old World*. American Committee for International Wild Life Protection, New York, 1945.

HARRIS, WILLIAM CORNWALLIS, Sir. *Portraits of the Game and Wild Animals of Southern African*. London, 1840.

HEYNIUS-VIRULY, Mrs and F. C. VAN HEURN. *A Survey of Data Received from the Dutch Indies*. Special Publication of the American Committee for International Wild Life Protection, No. 8. Cambridge, Massachusetts, 1936.

INTERNATIONAL UNION FOR THE PROTECTION OF NATURE. See UNION INTERNATIONALE POUR LA PROTECTION DE LA NATURE.

JENNISON, GEORGE. *Animals for Show and Pleasure in Ancient Rome*. Manchester University Press, 1937.

KALM, PETER. *Travels into North America*. London, 1770-1.

LOCH, CHARLES W. '*Rhinoceros sondaicus*: Javan or Lesser One-horned Rhinoceros and its Geographical Distribution.' *Journal of the Malayan Branch of the Royal Asiatic Society*, Vol. 15, 1937. Singapore, 1938.

LYDEKKER, RICHARD. *The Game Animals of Africa* (2nd Edition, revised by J. G. Dollman). Rowland Ward, London, 1926.

MARSDEN, WILLIAM. *The History of Sumatra*. London, 1811.

MONCRIEFF, PERRINE. 'Bird Study in New Zealand.' *Oryx*, Vol. 1. Hertford, 1950-2.

MURPHY, ROBERT CUSHMAN. 'The Lost World of the Takahe.' *Natural History*, Vol. 58. American Museum of Natural History, New York, 1949.

NORDENSKIOLD, A. E. *The Voyage of the Vega round Asia and Europe*. (Translated by Alexander Leslie.) London, 1881.

ORBELL, G. B. 'Notornis Valley.' *Illustrated London News*, Vol. 214. London, 1949.

PEACOCK, E. H. *A Game-Book for Burma and Adjoining Territories*. Witherby, London, 1933.

PEARSON, T. GILBERT (Editor). *Birds of America*. Garden City Publishing Co., New York, 1936.

POCOCK, R. I. 'The Quagga.' *Journal of the Society for the Preservation of the Fauna of the Empire*, New Series, No. 2. London, 1922.

POLLOCK, F. T. and W. S. THOM. *Wild Sports of Burma and Assam*. London, 1900.

RENSHAW, GRAHAM. *Natural History Essays*. London, 1904.

BIBLIOGRAPHY

RENSHAW, GRAHAM. *More Natural History Essays.* London, 1905.

RENSHAW, GRAHAM. 'The Northern Sea-cow.' *Journal of the Society for the Preservation of the Fauna of the Empire*, New Series, No. 31. Hertford, 1937.

RENSHAW, GRAHAM. 'The Quagga.' *Journal of the Society for the Preservation of the Fauna of the Empire*, New Series, No. 26. Hertford, 1935.

RIDGEWAY, WILLIAM. 'Contributions to the Study of the Equidae; ii. On Hitherto Unrecorded Specimens of *Equus quagga*.' *Proceedings of the Zoological Society of London*, 1909.

SHEBBEARE, E. O. 'Status of the Three Asiatic Rhinoceros.' *Oryx*, Vol. 2. Hertford, 1953-4.

SHUFELDT, R. W. 'Anatomical and other Notes on the Passenger Pigeon (*Ectopistes migratorius*) lately living in the Cincinnati Zoological Gardens.' *Auk*, Vol. 32. American Ornithologists' Union, Cambridge, Massachusetts, 1915.

SIMPSON, GEORGE GAYLORD. *Horses.* Oxford University Press, New York, 1951.

SMITH, R. V. FRANCIS. 'Finding an "Extinct" New Zealand Bird.' *National Geographic Magazine*, Vol. 101. Washington, 1952.

SPARRMAN, ANDREW. *A Voyage to the Cape of Good Hope.* London, 1786.

STEJNEGER, LEONHARD. 'Contribution to the History of the Commander Islands, No. 1.—Notes on the Natural History, including descriptions of New Cetaceans.' *Proceedings of the United States National Museum*, Vol. 6, 1883. Washington, 1884.

STEJNEGER, LEONHARD. 'Contributions to the History of the Commander Islands. No. 2.—Investigations Relating to the Extermination of Steller's Sea-Cow.' *Proceedings of the United States National Museum*, Vol. 7, 1884. Washington, 1885.

STEJNEGER, LEONHARD. *Georg Wilhelm Steller: The Pioneer of Alaskan Natural History.* Harvard University Press, Cambridge, Massachusetts, 1936.

STEJNEGER, LEONHARD. 'How the great northern sea-cow (Rytina) became exterminated.' *American Naturalist*, Vol. 21. Philadelphia, 1887.

STELLER, GEORG WILHELM. *De Bestiis Marinis.* Petrograd, 1751.

STELLER, GEORG WILHELM. *Journal of the Sea Voyage from Kamchatka to America and Return on the Second Expedition*, 1741-1742. Translated and in part annotated by Leonhard Stejneger. Included in Bering's Voyages by F. A. Golder (q.v.)

TURBOTT, E. G. 'Rediscovery of *Notornis*.' *Agenda and Abstracts of the Scientific Meetings of the Zoological Society of London*, 1954, No. 5.

UNION INTERNATIONALE POUR LA PROTECTION DE LA NATURE. *Les Fossiles de Demain.* Brussels, 1954.

UNION INTERNATIONALE POUR LA PROTECTION DE LA NATURE. *Proceedings and Papers of the International Technical Conference on the Protection of Nature, Lake Success, 1949.* Paris and Brussels, 1950.

UNION INTERNATIONALE POUR LA PROTECTION DE LA NATURE. *The Position of Nature Protection throughout the World in 1950.* Brussels, 1951.

WILLIAMS, G. R. 'An Almost Extinct Bird.' *Discovery*, Vol. 11. London, 1950.

WILSON, ALEXANDER. *American Ornithology.* Philadelphia, 1808-14.

BIBLIOGRAPHY

Wisconsin Society for Ornithology. *Silent Wings: A Memorial to the Passenger Pigeon*. Wisconsin Society for Ornithology, Milwaukee, 1947.

Woodward, Henry. 'On an almost perfect Skeleton of *Rhytina gigas* (*Rhytina stelleri*, Steller's Sea-cow), obtained by Mr Robert Damon, F.G.S., from the Pleistocene Peat-deposits on Behring's Island.' *Quarterly Journal of the Geological Society of London*, Vol. 41. London, 1885.

Index

247

INDEX